Melvin Funk family

The Youth Hymnary

LESTER HOSTETLER, EDITOR

FAITH AND LIFE PRESS
Newton, Kansas
1956

Second Printing

Printed in the United States of America

PREFACE

Youth needs the inspiration of great music; youth needs also to grow in appreciation of great music. This youth hymnary is sent forth to fill a need in Sunday school, youth fellowships, summer Bible schools, or any other situation where youth gathers for worship and singing.

The Youth Hymnary supplements the Hymnary previously published and now in its ninth edition. The wide and careful selection of materials should assure ready acceptance and wide use of the book. The editor also deserves our gratitude for years of painstaking labor on the manuscript.

The hymns we sing unite us in Christian fellowship. The book is published with the earnest prayer that it will become a source of spiritual power and joy and that these songs may strengthen the Christian faith and life of the young people who use them.

Willard Claassen

INTRODUCTION

This book is intended for young people for use in the Sunday school, summer Bible school, Christian endeavor, youth fellowships, retreats, in fact for any worship service in church, home, or camp. Suitable material can be found for any age group from about nine years to twenty-five.

The theory underlying the choice of material is that young people should, for the most part, be taught songs of permanent worth that will last throughout life. This rules out many of the so-called "children's hymns" and leaves no rigid line between hymns for the young and hymns for older people.

Enthusiastic teachers know that young children can easily learn and will enjoy the grand hymns and hymn tunes if given an opportunity. Between the ages of nine to fifteen, especially, they memorize easily, and it is during this period that their impressionable minds should be well furnished with choice worship material found in the rich heritage of Christian hymnody. The memorization of the one hundred hymns found in the first part of the book—say at the rate of one per month—is highly recommended.

An examination of the Contents and Classification reveals the variety of material which is here assembled.

HYMNS. The first one hundred numbers consist of standard hymns which in subject matter follow the Christian Church Year. They are selected for their quality of music and sound biblical theology. Young people who will take the time to memorize these hymns will find them a source of joy and spiritual power throughout life and will find themselves prepared to participate in the worship of nearly any Protestant denomination, for good hymns know no denominational barriers.

DESCANTS. A number of the hymns have been provided with descants for optional use with groups that have at least a few high soprano voices to sing them. A descant is a counter melody above the regular melody. Its purpose is purely ornamental and its use should not be overdone. Adding a descant is one method of achieving variety in the singing of a hymn and stimulating new interest in it. A descant effect can be had in some hymns by asking the men to sing the melody while the sopranos sing the tenor part. Descants may be sung by a few soprano voices while the rest of the people sing the other parts; or all the sopranos may sing the descant while all the other people sing the regular melody, the organ filling out the harmony. It is not absolutely necessary to use words with a descant. A few high voices descanting with the syllable "Ah," with all the others singing the melody and the organ supplying the harmony, becomes very effective. The occasional singing of a hymn stanza in unison is also to be commended, for we need to find new and interesting ways of singing the old hymns, especially those that are long.

SPIRITUALS. After the hymn section there follows a group of spirituals, Negro and white, representing truly American music. They arose out of the hardships and sufferings of a people. It does not matter if you cannot sing a spiritual with the passion and the tone quality characteristic of Negro voices. Sing them your way. They reflect in a simple manner the universal needs of the human heart.

GOSPEL SONGS. The gospel songs had their origin and chief impetus in the Moody and Sankey revivals of the latter part of the nineteenth century. There are some authorities who question their usefulness today in the worship service because of the emphasis upon the "I," the introspective nature of the words, rather than the objective worship of the Most High. Nevertheless, they have been used of God to the blessing of multitudes of people, and are still worth knowing and can be used effectively, especially at the more informal meetings.

CAROLS. Numbers 153 to 182 are carols from all the nations drawn largely from the superb collection in the *Oxford Book of Carols* published by the Oxford Press. A carol, not easy of definition, has been described as a "religious seasonal song, of joyful character, in the vernacular and sung by the common people." They are associated with open air singing especially at Christmastime. Carols are always simple, sometimes crude in thought and expression, but they have survived for many generations. Their note of joy is much needed in our worship today. Their use need not be confined to Christmas or Easter. Many of them are suitable for other occasions and general use. Under the heading of each carol the appropriate time for its use is suggested.

PART SONGS. A large number of part songs, most of them for treble voices, are included. They can be used with girls' and unchanged boys' voices and are intended, for the most part, to be sung *a cappella,* that is, without accompaniment. Junior choirs and ladies choirs will find here a wealth of usable material. The use of part songs will stimulate music reading and develop the sense of harmony. Young children can easily learn to sing in parts, though the wise teacher will see to it that the parts are alternated so that young singers will not get the notion too early that they are either "sopranos" or "altos." A good introduction to part singing is through the use of a simple round. The boys' changing voices have been kept in mind and a number of pieces are included with easy bass well within their uncertain range of voice.

CANONS. A collection of canons (in their simplest forms called "rounds") has been added because choral groups love to sing them. In a canon the voice that begins the passage is closely imitated, note for note, by another voice or voices, beginning later and overlapping the first. A familiar example of a secular round we all know is "Three Blind Mice." The hymn tune *Tallis' Canon* (No. 100) is written in canonic form in that the tenor follows the soprano in exact imitation at a distance of four beats. The melody of a canon being the same in all parts, is quickly picked up and thus people who cannot read music at sight can yet share in the enjoyment of counter-part chorus singing. A canon, however simple, makes the highest demands upon the skill of the composer. Many of the great composers, for example Bach, Mozart, and Beethoven, made extensive use of this form of composition. Some of the numbers included here represent more complicated forms of the canon and are quite difficult but will interest the more advanced singers. A number of them are simple rounds which can be used effectively as table graces.

The Index of First Lines and the Contents and Classification will give assistance in making selections for special occasions and topics. Leaders and teachers who familiarize themselves with the book will have no difficulty in finding a variety of material for almost every kind of program.

The book is sent forth with the prayer that young people of a wide age range, and of all evangelical Christian denominations, will find its contents interesting, substantial, and a pleasure to use; and finally, what they have learned to sing as children and young people, will continue with them as an abiding joy and source of spiritual strength through all the days and years of their lives.

Lester Hostetler

ACKNOWLEDGMENTS

In the preparation of this book, covering a number of years, the editor has received invaluable help from musicians, ministers, and choir leaders. Dr. Evelyn Hohf, Professor of Music at Yankton College, served as musical advisor. Dr. J. Finley Williamson of the Westminster Choir School examined the manuscript in its early stages and gave valuable suggestions. The late Dr. Henry Sloan Coffin went over the material with me and gave helpful criticisms, as did Dr. and Mrs. Hugh Porter of Union Seminary in New York, and a former teacher, Dr. Clarence Dickinson and Mrs. Dickinson. Dr. Donald Kettring, author of "The Singing Church," was exceedingly helpful and kindly granted permission for the use of a number of his descants. Dr. Irvin Wolfe of Peabody College, an authority in public school music, gave me useful ideas and suggested sources of materials. Mr. Harold Moyer who became interested in the southern spirituals during his musical studies at Peabody College furnished most of the harmonizations for these numbers and checked the authenticity of the words and music. Mrs. Henry Dick assisted in the selection of the carols. The late Dr. Reginald McAll, then secretary of the Hymn Society of America, made available his collection of books and offered suggestions. Mrs. Ellis Graber and Mrs. Jacob Enz gave me the benefit of their training and experience with junior choirs. Others too numerous to mention have had a share in this undertaking, and I am grateful to all of them.

It is only fair to add that probably none of those who have given counsel and advice would approve every number that we finally included. That responsibility, with any errors of judgment, must rest with the editor and publishers.

Contents and Classification

ix

X

Part Songs for Treble Voices

Soprano, Alto, Bass

Two Part Songs

Responses and Choruses

HYMNS OF THE CHRISTIAN FAITH

1

Holy, Holy, Holy

NICÆA. 11. 12. 12. 10.

Reginald Heber, 1827
Descant with stanzas 2 and 4

John B. Dykes, 1861
Descant by Donald D. Kettring

Ho - - ly, Ho - - ly, Ho - - -

1. Ho-ly, Ho-ly, Ho-ly! Lord God Al-might - y! Ear - ly in the
2. Ho-ly, Ho-ly, Ho-ly! All the saints a-dore Thee, Cast-ing down their
3. Ho-ly, Ho-ly, Ho-ly! Tho' the dark-ness hide Thee, Tho' the eye of
4. Ho-ly, Ho-ly, Ho-ly! Lord God Al-might - y! All Thy works shall

- ly, Ho - - - ly, Ho - ly,

morn - ing our song shall rise to Thee; Ho - ly, Ho - ly, Ho - ly!
gold-en crowns a-round the glass - y sea; Cher - u - bim and ser-a-phim
sin - ful man Thy glo - ry may not see, On - ly Thou art ho - ly;
praise Thy name, in earth, and sky, and sea; Ho - ly, Ho - ly, Ho - ly!

Ho - - ly, Ho - ly, Ho - - ly! A-men.

Mer - ci - ful and Might - y! God in Three Per-sons, bless-ed Trin - i - ty!
fall - ing down be-fore Thee, Which wert, and art, and ev - er-more shalt be.
there is none be-side Thee Per - fect in power, in love, and pur - i - ty.
Mer - ci - ful and Might - y! God in Three Per-sons, bless-ed Trin - i - ty! A-men.

2 We Praise Thee, O God, Our Redeemer

KREMSER. 12. 11. 12. 11.

Julia Bulkley, 1902

Netherlands Folk Song, 1625
Arr. by Edward Kremser, 1835-1914

1. We praise Thee, O God, our Re - deem - er, Cre - a - tor,
2. We wor - ship Thee, God of our fa - thers, we bless Thee;
3. With voic - es u - ni - ted our prais - es we of - fer,

In grate - ful de - vo - tion our trib - ute we bring.
Thro' life's storm and tem - pest our Guide hast Thou been.
To Thee, great Je - ho - vah, glad an - thems we raise.

We lay it be - fore Thee, we kneel and a - dore Thee,
When per - ils o'er - take us, es - cape Thou wilt make us,
Thy strong arm will guide us, our God is be - side us,

We bless Thy ho - ly name, glad prais - es we sing.
And with Thy help, O Lord, our bat - tles we win.
To Thee, our great Re - deem - er, for - ev - er be praise. A - men.

ALTERNATIVE ENDING

All praise be Thine. A - men.

3 Now Let Every Tongue Adore Thee!

WACHET AUF. Irregular.

Philip Nicolai, 1556-1608
Tr. by Paul England, d. 1932
May be sung in unison

Philip Nicolai, 1556-1608

1. Now let ev - 'ry tongue a - dore Thee! Let men with an - gels
2. All Thy gates with pearl are glo - rious, Where we par - take through

sing be - fore Thee! Let harps and cym - bals now u - nite!
faith vic - to - rious, With an - gels round Thy throne of light.

3. No mor - tal eye hath seen. No mor - tal ear hath heard

Such won - drous things, There - fore with joy our song shall soar

In praise to God for - ev - er - more. A - men.

4 Praise to the Lord, the Almighty

LOBE DEN HERREN. P. M.

Joachim Neander, 1680
Tr. by Catherine Winkworth, 1863

"Stralsund Gesangbuch," 1665
Present form since 1708

1. Praise to the Lord, the Al-might-y, the King of cre-a - tion!
2. Praise to the Lord! who o'er all things so won-drous-ly reign - eth,
3. Praise to the Lord! who doth pros-per thy work and de - fend thee;
4. Praise to the Lord! O let all that is in me a - dore Him!

O my soul, praise Him, for He is thy health and sal - va - tion!
Shel-ters thee un - der His wings, yea, so gent - ly sus - tain - eth;
Sure - ly His good-ness and mer - cy here dai - ly at - tend thee.
All that hath life and breath, come now with prais-es be - fore Him!

All ye who hear, Now to His tem - ple draw near!
Hast thou not seen How thy en - trea - ties have been
Pon - der a - new What the Al - might - y can do,
Let the A - men Sound from His peo - ple a - gain;

Praise Him in glad ad - o - ra - tion.
Grant - ed in what He or - dain - eth?
If with His love He be - friend thee!
Glad - ly for aye we a - dore Him. A - men.

5

A Mighty Fortress Is Our God

EIN' FESTE BURG. 8. 7. 8. 7. 6. 6. 6. 6. 7.

Martin Luther, 1483-1546
Tr. by Frederick H. Hedge, 1805-1890

Martin Luther, 1483-1546

1. A might-y for-tress is our God, A bul-wark nev-er fail-ing;
2. Did we in our own strength con-fide, Our striv-ing would be los-ing;
3. And though this world, with dev-ils filled, Should threat-en to un-do us,
4. That word a-bove all earth-ly powers, No thanks to them, a-bid-eth;

Our help-er He, a-mid the flood Of mor-tal ills pre-vail-ing.
Were not the right Man on our side, The Man of God's own choos-ing.
We will not fear, for God hath willed His truth to tri-umph through us.
The Spir-it and the gifts are ours Through Him who with us sid-eth.

For still our an-cient foe Doth seek to work us woe; His craft and power are
Dost ask who that may be? Christ Je-sus, it is He, Lord Sab-a-oth His
The Prince of Dark-ness grim—We trem-ble not for him; His rage we can en-
Let goods and kin-dred go, This mor-tal life al-so; The bod-y they may

great; And armed with cru-el hate, On earth is not his e-qual.
name, From age to age the same, And He must win the bat-tle.
dure, For lo! his doom is sure; One lit-tle word shall fell him.
kill. God's truth a-bid-eth still; His king-dom is for-ev-er. A-men.

6 ## Now Thank We All Our God

NUN DANKET. 6. 7. 6. 7. 6. 6. 6. 6.

Martin Rinkart, 1636
Tr. by Catherine Winkworth, 1858

Johann Crüger, 1648

Descant with stanza 3

1. Now thank we all our God With heart and hands and voic-es,
2. O may this boun-teous God Through all our life be near us,
3. All praise and thanks to God, The Fa-ther, now be giv-en,

Who won-drous things hath done, In whom His world re-joic-es;
With ev-er joy-ful hearts And bless-ed peace to cheer us;
The Son, and Him who reigns With them in high-est heav-en,

Who, from our moth-ers' arms Hath blessed us on our way
And keep us in His grace, And guide us when per-plexed,
The one e-ter-nal God, Whom earth and heav'n a-dore;

With count-less gifts of love, And still is ours to-day.
And free us from all ills In this world and the next.
For thus it was, is now, And shall be ev - er - more. A - men.

Descant copyrighted by United Church Pub. House, Toronto. Used by permission.

7 O Worship the King

LYONS. 10. 10 11. 11.

Robert Grant, 1833

Arr. from Michael Haydn, 1770

1. O wor - ship the King, all glo-rious a - bove, O grate-ful - ly
2. O tell of His might, O sing of His grace, Whose robe is the
3. Thy boun - ti - ful care what tongue can re - cite? It breathes in the
4. Frail chil - dren of dust, and fee - ble as frail, In Thee do we

sing His power and His love; Our Shield and De - fend - er, the An-cient of
light, whose can - o - py space. His char - iots of wrath the deep thun-der-clouds
air, it shines in the light, It streams from the hills, it de-scends to the
trust, nor find Thee to fail; Thy mer-cies how ten-der! how firm to the

Days, Pa - vil - ioned in splen-dor, and gird - ed with praise.
form, And dark is His path on the wings of the storm.
plain, And sweet - ly dis - tills in the dew and the rain.
end! Our Mak - er, De - fend - er, Re - deem-er and Friend. A - men.

8 Sing Praise to God Who Reigns Above

MIT FREUDEN ZART. 8. 7. 8. 7. 8. 8. 7.

Johann J. Schütz, 1640-1690
Tr. Frances E. Cox, 1812-1897

From the "Bohemian Brethren's
Gesangbuch," 1566

In Unison

1. Sing praise to God who reigns a-bove, The God of all cre - a - tion,
2. What God's al-might - y pow'r hath made, His gra-cious mer - cy keep-eth;
3. The Lord is nev - er far a - way, But, through all grief dis - tress - ing,
4. Thus, all my toil - some way a - long, I sing a - loud Thy prais - es,

The God of pow'r, the God of love, The God of our sal -
By morn - ing glow or eve - ning shade His watch-ful eye ne'er
An ev - er - pres - ent help and stay, Our peace, and joy, and
That men may hear the grate - ful song My voice un - wea - ried

va - tion; With heal-ing balm my soul He fills, And ev - 'ry faith-less
sleep - eth; With - in the king-dom of His might, Lo! all is just and
bless - ing; As with a moth-er's ten-der hand, He leads His own, His
rais - es; Be joy - ful in the Lord, my heart, Both soul and bod - y

mur - mur stills: To God all praise and glo - ry.
all is right: To God all praise and glo - ry.
cho - sen band: To God all praise and glo - ry.
bear your part: To God all praise and glo - ry. A - men.

9 Holy God, We Praise Thy Name

GROSSER GOTT, WIR LOBEN DICH. 7. 8. 7. 8. 7. 7.

Te Deum
Tr. Clarence Walworth, 1820-1900

"Katholiches Gesangbuch," Vienna, 1774

1. Ho - ly God, we praise Thy name; Lord of all, we bow be-fore Thee;
2. Hark, the loud ce - les - tial hymn, An - gel choirs a - bove are rais-ing;
3. Lo! the ap - os - tol - ic train, Joins Thy sa - cred name to hal - low;
4. Ho - ly Fa - ther, Ho - ly Son, Ho - ly Spir - it, Three we name Thee;

All on earth Thy scep - ter claim, All in heav'n a - bove a - dore Thee.
Cher - u - bim and Ser - a - phim, In un - ceas - ing cho - rus prais-ing,
Proph - ets swell the glad re - frain, And the white-robed mar-tyrs fol - low;
While in es - sence on - ly One, Un - di - vid - ed God we claim Thee,

In - fi - nite Thy vast do - main, Ev - er - last - ing is Thy reign.
Fill the heav'ns with sweet ac - cord: Ho - ly, ho - ly, ho - ly Lord.
And, from morn to set of sun, Through the Church the song goes on.
And a - dor - ing bend the knee, While we sing our praise to Thee. A - men.

Grosser Gott, wir loben Dich

1 Grosser Gott, wir loben Dich!
   Herr, wir preisen Deine Stärke!
   Vor Dir neigt die Erde sich
   Und bewundert Deine Werke.
   Wie Du warst vor aller Zeit,
   So bleibst Du in Ewigkeit!

2 Auf dem ganzen Erdenkreis
   Loben Grosse Dich and Kleine.
   Dir, Gott Vater, Dir zum Preis
   Singt die heilige Gemeine,
   Und verehrt auf Seinem Thron
   Deinen eingebornen Sohn.

3 Sie verehrt den heil'gen Geist,
   Welcher uns mit Seinen Lehren
   Und mit Trost gar kräftig speist,
   Dich, den Herrscher voller Ehren
   Der mit Dir, o Jesu Christ,
   Und dem Vater Eines ist!

4 Stehe denn, o Herr, uns bei,
   Die wir Dich in Demut bitten:
   Sprich von aller Schuld uns frei,
   Da Du auch für uns gelitten;
   Nimm uns nach vollbrachtem Lauf
   Zu Dir in den Himmel auf!

10 Give to Our God Immortal Praise

LASST UNS ERFREUEN. 8. 8. 4. 4. 8. 8. with Alleluias.

Founded on Psalm 136
Isaac Watts, 1674-1748
Descant with stanzas 3 and 5

Melody from
"Geistliche Kirchengesänge," 1623
Descant by Donald D. Kettring

Unison

3. He built the earth and spread the sky   And
5. Give   to our God immortal praise   Mer -

1. Give   to our God im - mor - tal   praise;   Mer - cy   and truth are all His
2. Give   to the Lord of lords re - nown;   The   King   of kings with glo - ry
3. He   built the earth, He spread the   sky,   And   fixed   the star - ry lights on
4. He   fills the sun with morn - ing   light,   He   bids   the moon di - rect the
5. Give   to our God im - mor - tal   praise;   Mer - cy   and truth are all His

fixed the stars on high   Hal - le - lu - jah
cy and truth are all His ways   *Unison*

Harmony

ways;   Hal - le - lu - jah, Hal - le - lu - jah!   Won - ders of grace to
crown: His   mer - cies ev - er
high: Won - ders of grace to
night: His   mer - cies ev - er
ways;   Won - ders of grace to

Won-ders of grace to God be-long   Re - peat His mercies in your song

Harmony

God be - long,   Re - peat His mer-cies in your song: Hal - le - lu - jah,
shall en - dure,   When lords and kings are known no more:
God be - long,   Re - peat His mer-cies in your song:
shall en - dure,   When sun and moon shall shine no more:
God be - long,   Re - peat His mer-cies in your song:

Hal-le - lu - jah, Hal-le - lu - jah, Hal-le-lu - jah, Hal-le-lu - jah. A-men.

Unison   *Harmony*

Hal-le - lu - jah, Hal-le-lu - jah, Hal-le-lu - jah, Hal-le - lu - jah! A-men.

Descant copyrighted. Used by permission of the composer.

11 Come, Thou Almighty King

ITALIAN HYMN. 6. 6. 4. 6. 6. 6. 4.

Charles Wesley, 1757   Felice De Giardini, 1769

1. Come, Thou al - might - y King, Help us Thy name to sing,
2. Come, Thou In - car - nate Word, Gird on Thy might - y sword,
3. Come, Ho - ly Com - fort - er, Thy sa - cred wit - ness bear,
4. To Thee, great One in Three, E - ter - nal prais - es be

Help us to praise! Fa - ther all - glo - ri - ous, O'er all vic -
Our pray'r at - tend; Come, and Thy peo - ple bless, And give Thy
In this glad hour: Thou who al - might - y art, Now rule in
Hence, ev - er - more: Thy sov-'reign maj - es - ty May we in

to - ri - ous, Come, and reign o - ver us, An - cient of Days!
word suc-cess; Spir - it of ho - li - ness, On us de - scend!
ev - ery heart, And ne'er from us de - part, Spir - it of power!
glo - ry see, And to e - ter - ni - ty Love and a - dore! A - men.

12 Unto the Hills

SANDON. 10. 4. 10. 4. 10. 10.

Psalm CXXI.
John Campbell, 1845-1914

Charles Purday, 1799-1885

1. Un - to the hills a - round do I lift up My long - ing eyes:
2. He will not suf - fer that thy foot be moved: Safe shalt thou be.
3. Je - ho - vah is Him - self thy keep - er true, Thy change-less shade!
4. From ev - 'ry e - vil shall He keep thy soul, From ev - 'ry sin:

O whence for me shall my sal - va - tion come, From whence a - rise?
No care - less slum - ber shall His eye - lids close, Who keep - eth thee.
Je - ho - vah thy de - fense on thy right hand Him - self hath made.
Je - ho - vah shall pre - serve thy go - ing out, Thy com - ing in.

From God the Lord doth come my cer - tain aid,
Be - hold, He sleep - eth not, He slum - b'reth ne'er,
And thee no sun by day shall ev - er smite;
A - bove thee watch - ing, He whom we a - dore

From God the Lord who heav'n and earth hath made.
Who keep - eth Is - rael in His ho - ly care.
No moon shall harm thee in the si - lent night.
Shall keep thee hence - forth, yea, for - ev - er - more. A-men.

13   O Come, O Come Emmanuel

VENI EMMANUEL. 8. 8. 8. 8. 8. 8.

From Latin, 12th Century
V. 1 Tr. by J. M. Neale, 1851
vv. 2 and 3 tr. by Henry S. Coffin, 1916

Ancient Plain Song
13th Century

In Unison

1. O come, O come, Em - man - u - el, And ran - som cap - tive
2. O come, Thou Wis - dom from on high, And or - der all things,
3. O come, De - sire of na - tions, bind All peo - ples in one

Is - ra - el, That mourns in lone - ly ex - ile here,
far and nigh; To us the path of knowl - edge show,
heart and mind; Bid en - vy, strife and quar - rels cease;

In Harmony

Un - til the Son of God ap - pear. Re - joice! Re - joice! Em -
And cause us in her ways to go. Re - joice! Re - joice! Em -
Fill all the world with heav - en's peace. Re - joice! Re - joice! Em -

man - u - el Shall come to thee, O Is - ra - el! A-men.

14 Joy to the World!

ANTIOCH. C. M. D.

Isaac Watts, 1719

Arr. by Lowell Mason, 1833
Descant by Russell Carter

1. Joy to the world! the Lord is come; Let earth re-
2. Joy to the world! the Sav - ior reigns; Let men their
3. He rules the world with truth and grace, And makes the

Al - le - lu – ia! Al - le - lu - ia!

ceive her King; Let ev - ery heart pre - pare Him room,
songs em - ploy; While fields and floods, rocks, hills and plains
na - tions prove The glo - ries of His right - eous - ness,

Al - le - lu - ia! Al -

And heaven and na - ture sing, And heaven and na - ture
Re - peat the sound - ing joy, Re - peat the sound - ing
And won - ders of His love, And won - ders of His

And heaven and na - ture sing, And

le - lu - ia!

sing, And heaven, and heaven and na - ture sing.
joy, Re - peat, re - peat the sound - ing joy.
love, And won - ders, and won - ders of His love.

heaven and na - ture sing,

15 Come, Thou Long Expected Jesus

HYFRYDOL. 8. 7. 8. 7. D.

Charles Wesley, 1744
Descant with stanza 2

Rowland H. Prichard, 1811-1887
Descant by Alan Gray

1. Come, Thou long - ex - pect - ed Je - sus, Born to set Thy peo - ple free;
2. Born Thy peo - ple to de - liv - er, Born a child and yet a King,

From our fears and sins re - lease us! Let us find our rest in Thee.
Born to reign in us for - ev - er, Now Thy gra - cious king - dom bring.

Is - rael's Strength and Con - so - la - tion, Hope of all the earth Thou art;
By Thine own e - ter - nal Spir - it Rule in all our hearts a - lone;

Dear De - sire of ev - ery na - tion, Joy of ev - ery long - ing heart.
By Thine all suf - fi - cient mer - it Raise us to Thy glo - rious throne. A - men.

16 O Come, All Ye Faithful

ADESTE FIDELES. Irregular.

Latin hymn, 17th century
Tr. Frederick Oakley, 1841

John F. Wade's "Cantus Diversi," 1751

1. O come, all ye faith-ful, joy-ful and tri-um-phant, O come ye to Beth-le-hem with one glad ac-cord. Lo! in a man-ger lies the King of an-gels; O come let us a-dore Him, O come let us a-dore Him, O come let us a-dore Him, Christ the Lord. A-men.

2. Sing, choirs of an-gels, sing in ex-ul-ta-tion, Sing, all ye that hear in heav-en God's ho-ly word. Give to our Fa-ther glo-ry in the high-est; O come let us a-dore Him, O come let us a-dore Him,

3. Hail! Lord, we greet Thee, born this hap-py morn-ing, O Je-sus! for ev-er-more be Thy name a-dored. Word of the Fa-ther, now in flesh ap-pear-ing, O come let us a-dore Him, O come let us a-dore Him,

17 O Little Town of Bethlehem

ST. LOUIS. 8. 6. 8. 6. 7. 6. 8. 6.

Phillips Brooks, 1868

Lewis H. Redner, 1865

1. O lit - tle town of Beth - le - hem, How still we see thee lie!
2. For Christ is born of Ma - - ry, And gath - ered all a - bove,
3. How si - lent - ly, how si - lent - ly, The won - drous gift is giv'n!
4. O ho - ly Child of Beth - le - hem! De - scend to us, we pray;

A - bove thy deep and dream-less sleep The si - lent stars go by!
While mor - tals sleep, the an - gels keep Their watch of won-d'ring love.
So God im - parts to hu - man hearts The bless - ings of His heav'n.
Cast out our sin, and en - ter in; Be born in us to - day.

Yet in thy dark streets shin - eth The ev - er - last - ing Light;
O morn - ing stars, to - geth - er Pro - claim the ho - ly birth!
No ear may hear His com - ing, But in this world of sin,
We hear the Christ - mas an - gels The great glad ti - dings tell;

The hopes and fears of all the years Are met in thee to - night.
And prais - es sing to God the King, And peace to men on earth.
Where meek souls will re - ceive Him still, The dear Christ en - ters in.
O come to us, a - bide with us, Our Lord Em - man - u - el. A-men.

18 Break Forth O Beauteous Heav'nly Light

SCHOP. 8. 7. 8. 7. 8. 8. 7. 7.

Johann Rist, 1641
Joyously; may be sung in unison

Johann Schop, 1641
Har. J. S. Bach, 1734

Break forth, O beau-teous heav'n-ly light, And ush-er in the morn-ing; Ye shep-herds, shrink not with af-fright, But hear the an-gel's warn-ing. This child, this lit-tle help-less boy, Shall be our con-fi-dence and joy, The powers of hell o'er-throw-ing, At last our peace be-stow-ing.

19 Angels, from the Realms of Glory

REGENT SQUARE. 8. 7. 8. 7. 4. 7.

James Montgomery, 1819

Henry Smart, 1867

1. An - gels, from the realms of glo - ry, Wing your flight o'er
2. Shep - herds, in the field a - bid - ing, Watch - ing o'er your
3. Sa - ges leave your con - tem - pla - tions, Bright - er vis - ions
4. Saints be - fore the al - tar bend - ing, Watch - ing long in

all the earth; Ye who sang cre - a - tion's sto - ry,
flocks by night, God with man is now re - sid - ing,
beam a - far; Seek the great De - sire of na - tions;
hope and fear, Sud - den - ly the Lord, de - scend - ing,

Now pro - claim Mes - si - ah's birth: Come and wor - ship,
Yon - der shines the in - fant Light: Come and wor - ship,
Ye have seen His na - tal star: Come and wor - ship,
In His tem - ple shall ap - pear: Come and wor - ship,

Come and wor - ship, Wor - ship Christ, the new - born King. A - men.

20 The First Noel the Angel Did Say

THE FIRST NOEL. Irregular with Refrain.

Traditional
Descant with stanzas 3 and 5

Traditional

No - el,— No - el!

1. The first No - el the an - gel did say Was to cer - tain poor
2. They look - ed up and saw a star Shin - ing in the
3. And by the light of that same star, Three wise men
4. This star drew nigh to the north-west, O'er Beth - le -
5. Then en - tered in those wise men three, Full re - ver - ent -

No - el, No - el! No - el,— No -

shep-herds in fields as they lay; In fields where they lay keep - ing their
east, be - yond them far, And to the earth it gave great
came from coun - try far; To seek for a king was their in -
hem it took its rest, And there it did both stop and
ly up - on the knee, And of - fered there, in His pres -

el! No - el, No - el! No-el, No-

Refrain

sheep, On a cold win-ter's night that was so deep.
light, And so it con - tin - ued both day and night.
tent, And to fol - low the star wher - ev - er it went. No - el, No -
stay, Right o - ver the place where Je - sus lay.
ence, Their gold, and myrrh, and frank - in-cense.

el, No - el, No - el!—   No - el, No - el!
el, No - el, No - el,   Born is the King of Is - ra - el.

Descant from "The American Singer." Used by permission of the American Book Co.

21   There's a Song in the Air!

CHRISTMAS SONG.   6. 6. 6. 6. 12. 12.

Josiah G. Holland, 1819-1881   Karl P. Harrington, 1861-

1. There's a song in the air! There's a star in the sky! There's a moth-er's deep
2. There's a tu-mult of joy O'er the won-der-ful birth, For the Vir-gin's sweet
3. In the light of that star Lie the a-ges im-pearled; And that song from a
4. We re-joice in the light, And we ech - o the song That comes down thro' the

prayer And a ba-by's low cry! And the star rains its fire while the
boy Is the Lord of the earth. Ay! the star rains its fire while the
far Has swept o - ver the world. Ev - er-y hearth is a - flame, and the
night From the heav - en - ly throng. Ay! we shout to the love - ly e -

beau - ti - ful sing, For the man - ger of Beth-le - hem cra-dles a King!
beau - ti - ful sing, For the man - ger of Beth-le - hem cra-dles a King!
beau - ti - ful sing In the homes of the na-tions that Je - sus is King!
van - gel they bring, And we greet in His cra - dle our Sav-iour and King!

Words used by permission of Charles Scribner's Sons.
Music copyright by Karl P. Harrington. Renewal, 1933.

22 Silent Night! Holy Night!

STILLE NACHT. Irregular.

Joseph Mohr, 1818
Tr. compiled

Franz Gruber, 1818

1. Si - lent night, ho - ly night, All is calm, all is bright;
2. Si - lent night, ho - ly night, Dark - ness flies, all is light;
3. Si - lent night, ho - ly night, Son of God, love's pure light;
4. Si - lent night, ho - ly night, Won - drous Star, lend thy light;

Round yon Vir - gin Moth - er and Child! Ho - ly In - fant, so ten-der and mild,
Shep - herds hear the an - gels sing, "Al - le - lu - ia! hail the King!
Ra - diant beams from Thy ho - ly face, With the dawn of re - deem - ing grace,
With the an - gels let us sing, Al - le - lu - ia to our King;

Sleep in heav - en - ly peace,   Sleep in heav - en - ly peace.
Christ the Sav - iour is born,   Christ the Sav - iour is born."
Je - sus, Lord, at Thy birth,   Je - sus, Lord, at Thy birth.
Christ the Sav - iour is born,   Christ the Sav - iour is born.

Stille Nacht, heilige Nacht!

1 Stille Nacht, heilige Nacht!
Alles schläft, einsam wacht,
Nur das fromme so selige Paar,
Das im Stalle zu Bethlehem war
:Bei dem himmlischen Kind.:

2 Stille Nacht, heilige Nacht!
Hirten wird's kund gemacht;
Durch der Engel Hallelujah
Tönt es laut von ferne und nah.
:Jesus der Retter ist da.:

3 Stille Nacht, heilige Nacht!
Gottes Sohn!—o wie lacht
Lieb' aus deinem holdseligen Mund,
Da uns schläget die rettende Stund;
:Christ in deiner Geburt.:

4 Stille Nacht, heilige Nacht!
Erd' erwach' aus dem Schlaf,
Hoch ertön' in melodischem Klang,
Hoch zum Himmel dein Jubelgesang,
:Friede auf immer der Welt.:

23 What Child Is This, Who, Laid to Rest

CHRIST THE KING. 8. 7. 8. 7. with Refrain.

Traditional
Arr. William C. Dix, 1837-1898

Old English Melody

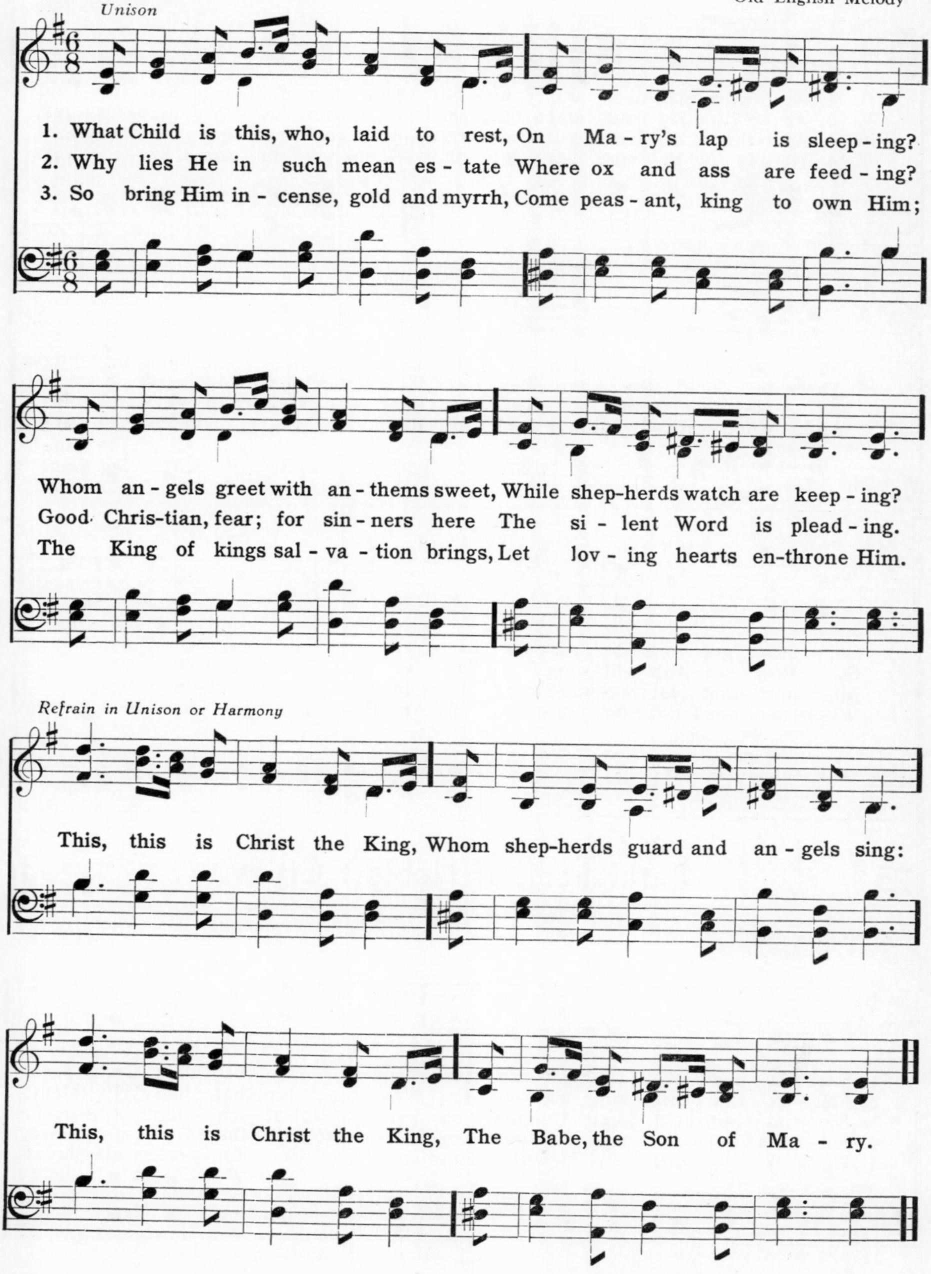

Unison

1. What Child is this, who, laid to rest, On Ma - ry's lap is sleep - ing?
2. Why lies He in such mean es - tate Where ox and ass are feed - ing?
3. So bring Him in - cense, gold and myrrh, Come peas - ant, king to own Him;

Whom an - gels greet with an - thems sweet, While shep-herds watch are keep - ing?
Good Chris-tian, fear; for sin - ners here The si - lent Word is plead - ing.
The King of kings sal - va - tion brings, Let lov - ing hearts en-throne Him.

Refrain in Unison or Harmony

This, this is Christ the King, Whom shep-herds guard and an - gels sing:

This, this is Christ the King, The Babe, the Son of Ma - ry.

24 As With Gladness Men of Old

DIX. 7. 7. 7. 7. 7. 7.

William C. Dix, 1861

Arr. from Conrad Kocher, 1838

1. As with glad-ness men of old Did the guid-ing star be-hold;
2. As with joy-ous steps they sped To that low-ly man-ger-bed,
3. As they of-fered gifts most rare, At that man-ger rude and bare,
4. Ho-ly Je-sus, ev-'ry day Keep us in the nar-row way;

As with joy they hailed its light, Lead-ing on-ward, beam-ing bright;
There to bend the knee be-fore Him whom heav'n and earth a-dore;
So may we with ho-ly joy, Pure and free from sin's al-loy,
And, when earth-ly things are past, Bring our ran-somed souls at last—

So, most gra-cious Lord, may we Ev-er-more be led to Thee.
So may we with will-ing feet Ev-er seek Thy mer-cy-seat.
All our cost-liest treas-ures bring, Christ, to Thee, our heav'n-ly King.
Where they need no star to guide, Where no clouds Thy glo-ry hide. A-men.

25 Bethlehem, of Noblest Cities

STUTTGART. 8. 7. 8. 7.

Prudentius, b. 348
Tr. E. Caswall, 1849

"Psalmodia Sacra," Gotha, 1715
Adapted

1. Beth-le-hem, of no-blest cit-ies None can once with thee com-pare;
2. Fair-er than the sun at morn-ing Was the star that told His birth;
3. By its lam-bent beau-ty guid-ed See the East-ern kings ap-pear;
4. Sol-emn things of mys-tic mean-ing: In-cense doth the God dis-close,
5. Ho-ly Je-sus, in Thy bright-ness To the Gen-tile world dis-played,

Thou a - lone the Lord from heav - en Didst for us in - car-nate bear.
To the lands their God an-nounc-ing, Hid be-neath a form of earth.
See them bend, their gifts to of - fer, Gifts of in-cense, gold, and myrrh.
Gold a roy - al Child pro-claim-eth, Myrrh a fu - ture tomb fore-shows.
With the Fa - ther and the Spir - it End-less praise to Thee be paid. A-men.

The Presentation in the Temple

26 When Mary Brought Her Treasure

AVE MARIA KLARE. 7. 6. 7. 6. 6. 7. 6.

Jan Struther, 1901-53

Psalteriolum Harmonicum, 1642

1. When Ma - ry brought her treas - ure Un - to the ho - ly place,
2. Then Sim - eon on him gaz - ing With won - der and with love,
3. And she, all sor - row scorn - ing, Re - joiced in Je - sus' fame.
4. As by the sun in splen - dor The flags of night are furled,

No eye of man could meas-ure The joy up - on her face. He was but
His a - ged voice up - rais - ing Gave thanks to God a - bove: 'Now wel-come
The child her arms a - dorn-ing Shone soft - ly like a flame That burns the
So dark-ness shall sur - ren - der To Christ who lights the world: To Christ the

six weeks old, Her play-thing and her pleas-ure, Her sil - ver and her gold.
sweet re - lease! For I, my Sav-iour prais-ing, May die at last in peace.
long night through, And keeps from dusk till morn-ing Its vig - il clear and true.
Star of day, Who once was small and ten-der, A can-dle's gen-tle ray.

27 Forty Days and Forty Nights

HEINLEIN. 7. 7. 7. 7.

George H. Smyttan, 1856, alt.

Nürnbergisches Gesangbuch, 1676

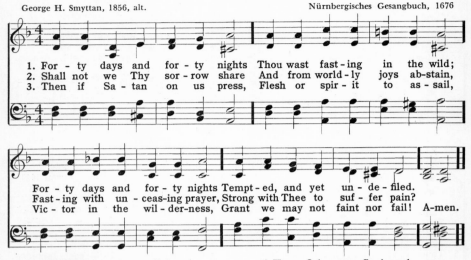

1. For - ty days and for - ty nights Thou wast fast-ing in the wild;
2. Shall not we Thy sor - row share And from world - ly joys ab-stain,
3. Then if Sa - tan on us press, Flesh or spir - it to as - sail,

For - ty days and for - ty nights Tempt - ed, and yet un - de - filed.
Fast-ing with un - ceas-ing prayer, Strong with Thee to suf - fer pain?
Vic - tor in the wil - der-ness, Grant we may not faint nor fail! A-men.

4 So shall we have peace divine:
Holier gladness ours shall be;
Round us, too, shall angels shine,
Such as ministered to Thee.

5 Keep, O keep us, Saviour dear,
Ever constant by Thy side;
That with Thee we may appear
At th'eternal Eastertide.

28 My Soul, Be On Thy Guard

HEATH. S. M.

George Heath, 1781

Mason and Webb's
"Cantica Laudis," 1850

1. My soul, be on thy guard; Ten thou - sand foes a - rise;
2. O watch and fight and pray! The bat - tle ne'er give o'er;
3. Ne'er think the vic - tory won, Nor lay thine ar - mor down:
4. Fight on, my soul, till death Shall bring thee to thy God!

A host of sins are press-ing hard To draw thee from the skies.
Re - new it bold - ly ev - 'ry day, And help di - vine im - plore.
Thy ar - duous work will not be done Till thou ob - tain thy crown.
He'll take thee, at thy part - ing breath, Up to His blest a - bode.

29 All Glory, Laud, and Honor

ST. THEODULPH. 7. 6. 7. 6. D.

Theodulph of Orleans, c. 820
Tr. John M. Neale, 1854

Melchior Teschner, 1615

All glo - ry, laud, and hon - or To Thee, Re - deem - er, King,
To whom the lips of chil - dren Made sweet ho - san - nas ring.

1. Thou art the King of Is - rael, Thou Da - vid's roy - al Son,
2. The com - pa - ny of an - gels Are prais - ing Thee on high,
3. The peo - ple of the He - brews With palms be - fore Thee went;
4. To Thee, be - fore Thy pas - sion, They sang their hymns of praise;
5. Thou didst ac - cept their prais - es; Ac - cept the prayers we bring,

Who in the Lord's name com - est, The King and Bless - ed One.
And mor - tal men, and all things Cre - at - ed, make re - ply.
Our praise and prayer and an - thems Be - fore Thee we pre - sent.
To Thee, now high ex - alt - ed, Our mel - o - dy we raise.
Who in all good de - light - est, Thou good and gra - cious King.

Refrain

All glo - ry, laud, and hon - or To Thee, Re - deem - er, King,
To whom the lips of chil - dren Made sweet ho - san - nas ring. A-men.

Palm Sunday

30 Ride on, Ride on, in Majesty

ST. DROSTANE. L. M.

Henry H. Milman, 1827   John B. Dykes, 1862

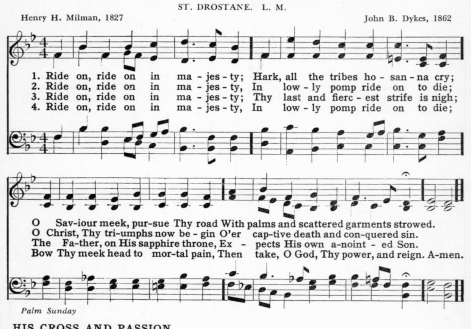

1. Ride on, ride on in ma-jes-ty; Hark, all the tribes ho-san-na cry;
2. Ride on, ride on in ma-jes-ty, In low-ly pomp ride on to die;
3. Ride on, ride on in ma-jes-ty; Thy last and fierc-est strife is nigh;
4. Ride on, ride on in ma-jes-ty, In low-ly pomp ride on to die;

O Sav-iour meek, pur-sue Thy road With palms and scattered garments strowed.
O Christ, Thy tri-umphs now be-gin O'er cap-tive death and con-quered sin.
The Fa-ther, on His sapphire throne, Ex - pects His own a-noint-ed Son.
Bow Thy meek head to mor-tal pain, Then take, O God, Thy power, and reign. A-men.

Palm Sunday

HIS CROSS AND PASSION

31 There Is a Green Hill Far Away

MEDITATION. C. M.

Cecil F. Alexander, 1848   John H. Gower, 1890

1. There is a green hill far a-way, With-out a cit-y wall,
2. We may not know, we can-not tell What pains He had to bear;
3. He died that we might be for-given; He died to make us good,
4. O dear-ly, dear-ly has He loved, And we must love Him, too,

Where the dear Lord was cru-ci-fied, Who died to save us all.
But we be-lieve it was for us He hung and suf-fered there.
That we might go at last to heaven, Saved by His pre-cious blood.
And trust in His re-deem-ing love, And try His works to do.

32

When I Survey the Wondrous Cross

HAMBURG. L. M.

Isaac Watts, 1707

From a Gregorian Chant
Arr. Lowell Mason, 1824

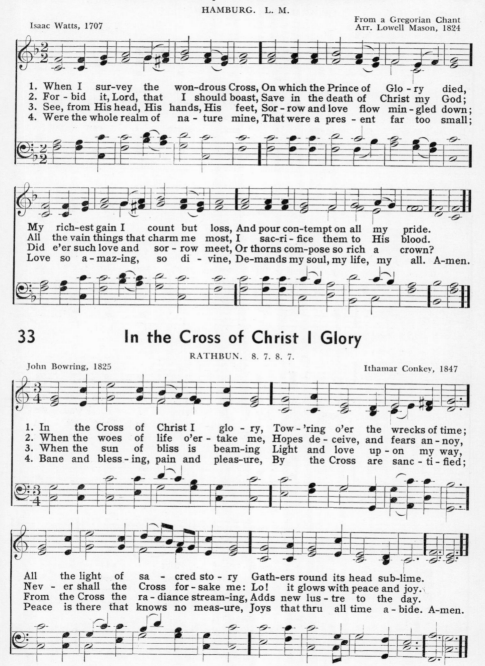

1. When I sur-vey the won-drous Cross, On which the Prince of Glo-ry died,
2. For-bid it, Lord, that I should boast, Save in the death of Christ my God;
3. See, from His head, His hands, His feet, Sor-row and love flow min-gled down;
4. Were the whole realm of na-ture mine, That were a pres-ent far too small;

My rich-est gain I count but loss, And pour con-tempt on all my pride.
All the vain things that charm me most, I sac-ri-fice them to His blood.
Did e'er such love and sor-row meet, Or thorns com-pose so rich a crown?
Love so a-maz-ing, so di-vine, De-mands my soul, my life, my all. A-men.

33

In the Cross of Christ I Glory

RATHBUN. 8. 7. 8. 7.

John Bowring, 1825

Ithamar Conkey, 1847

1. In the Cross of Christ I glo-ry, Tow-'ring o'er the wrecks of time;
2. When the woes of life o'er-take me, Hopes de-ceive, and fears an-noy,
3. When the sun of bliss is beam-ing Light and love up-on my way,
4. Bane and bless-ing, pain and pleas-ure, By the Cross are sanc-ti-fied;

All the light of sa-cred sto-ry Gath-ers round its head sub-lime.
Nev-er shall the Cross for-sake me: Lo! it glows with peace and joy.
From the Cross the ra-diance stream-ing, Adds new lus-tre to the day.
Peace is there that knows no meas-ure, Joys that thru all time a-bide. A-men.

34 Ah, Dearest Jesus, How Hast Thou Offended

HERZLIEBSTER JESU. 11. 11. 11. 5.

Johann Herrmann, c. 1630
Tr. Robert Bridges, 1899

Johann Crüger, 1640

1. Ah, dear-est Je-sus, how hast Thou of-fend-ed, That man to judge Thee hath in hate pre-tend-ed? By foes de-rid-ed, by Thine own re-ject-ed, O most af-flict-ed!

2. Who was the guilt-y? Who brought this up-on Thee? A-las, my trea-son, Je-sus, hath un-done Thee! 'Twas I, Lord Je-sus, I it was de-nied Thee: I cru-ci-fied Thee.

3. For me, dear Je-sus, was Thy in-car-na-tion, Thy mor-tal sor-row, and Thy life's ob-la-tion; Thy death of an-guish and Thy bit-ter pas-sion, For my sal-va-tion.

4. There-fore, dear Je-sus, since I can-not pay Thee, I do a-dore Thee, and will ev-er pray Thee, Think on Thy pit-y and Thy love un-swerv-ing, Not my de-serv-ing. A-men.

35   O Sacred Head, Now Wounded

PASSION CHORALE. 7. 6. 7. 6. D.

Bernard of Clairvaux, 1091-1153
Tr. Paul Gerhardt, 1656
Tr. J. W. Alexander, 1830

Hans Leo Hassler, 1601
Har. by J. S. Bach, 1719

1. O sa - cred Head, now wound - ed, With grief and shame weighed down,
2. What Thou, my Lord, hast suf - fered Was all for sin - ners' gain:
3. What lan - guage shall I bor - row To thank Thee, dear - est Friend,

Now scorn-ful - ly sur - round - ed With thorns, Thy on - ly crown,
Mine, mine was the trans - gres - sion, But Thine the dead - ly pain.
For this Thy dy - ing sor - row, Thy pit - y with - out end?

How art Thou pale with an - guish, With sore a - buse and scorn!
Lo, here I fall, my Sav - iour! 'Tis I de - serve Thy place;
O make me Thine for - ev - er; And, should I faint - ing be,

How does that vis - age lan - guish Which once was bright as morn!
Look on me with Thy fa - vor, Vouch - safe to me Thy grace.
Lord, let me nev - er, nev - er, Out - live my love to Thee! A-men.

36 Thine Is the Glory

5. 5. 6. 5. 6. 5. 6. 5. with Refrain.

Edmond Budry, 1884
Translated by R. Birch Hoyle, 1923

George Frederick Handel, 1685-1759

1. Thine is the glo-ry, Ris-en, con-qu'ring Son; End-less is the vic-t'ry Thou o'er death hast won. An-gels in bright rai-ment Rolled the stone a-way, Kept the fold-ed grave-clothes Where Thy bod-y lay.

2. Lo! Je-sus meets thee, Ris-en from the tomb; Lov-ing-ly He greets thee, Scat-ters fear and gloom; Let His church with glad-ness Hymns of tri-umph sing, For her Lord now liv-eth; Death hath lost its sting.

3. No more we doubt Thee, Glo-rious Prince of Life! Life is nought with-out Thee; Aid us in our strife; Make us more than con-qu'rors, Through Thy death-less love; Bring us safe through Jor-dan To Thy home a-bove.

Refrain

Thine is the glo-ry, Ris-en, con-qu'ring Son; End-less is the vic-t'ry Thou o'er death hast won. A-men.

37 Jesus Christ, Is Risen Today

EASTER HYMN. 7. 7. 7. 7. with Alleluia.

Charles Wesley, 1739

Arr. from Lyra Davidica, 1708

1. Je - sus Christ is ris'n to - day, Al - - le - lu - ia!
2. Hymns of praise then let us sing Al - - le - lu - ia!
3. But the pains which He en - dured, Al - - le - lu - ia!
4. Sing we to our God a - bove Al - - le - lu - ia!

Our tri - um - phant ho - ly day, Al - - le - lu - ia!
Un - to Christ, our heav'n-ly King, Al - - le - lu - ia!
Our sal - va - tion have pro - cured, Al - - le - lu - ia!
Praise e - ter - nal as His love; Al - - le - lu - ia!

Who did once up - on the Cross, Al - - le - lu - ia!
Who en - dured the Cross and grave, Al - - le - lu - ia!
Now a - bove the sky He's King, Al - - le - lu - ia!
Praise Him, all ye heav'n - ly host, Al - - le - lu - ia!

Suf - fer to re - deem our loss, Al - - le - lu - ia!
Sin - ners to re - deem and save. Al - - le - lu - ia!
Where the an-gels ev - er sing. Al - - le - lu - ia!
Fa - ther, Son, and Ho - ly Ghost. Al - - le - lu - ia! A - men.

38 Come, Ye Faithful, Raise the Strain

ST. KEVIN. 7. 6. 7. 6. D.

John of Damascus, c. 750
Tr. John M. Neale, 1850
Descant with stanza 3

Arthur S. Sullivan, 1872
Descant by Donald D. Kettring

1. Come, ye faith-ful, raise the strain Of tri-um-phant glad-ness:
2. 'Tis the spring of souls to-day: Christ hath burst His pris-on,
3. "Al-le-lu-ia!" now we cry To our King Im-mor-tal,

God hath brought His peo-ple forth In-to joy from sad-ness.
From the frost of gloom and death Light and life have ris-en.
Who, tri-um-phant, burst the bars Of the tomb's dark por-tal;

Now re-joice, Jer-u-sa-lem, And with true af-fec-tion
All the win-ter of our sins, Long and dark, is fly-ing
"Al-le-lu-ia!" with the Son, God the Fa-ther prais-ing

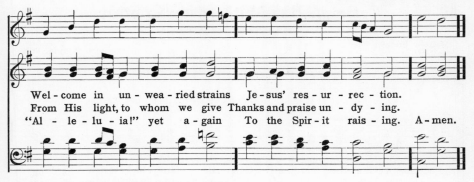

Wel - come in un - wea - ried strains Je - sus' res - ur - rec - tion.
From His light, to whom we give Thanks and praise un - dy - ing.
"Al - le - lu - ia!" yet a - gain To the Spir - it rais - ing. A - men.

Descant copyrighted. Used by permission of the composer.

39 The Strife Is O'er, the Battle Done

VICTORY. 8. 8. 8. with Alleluia.

Latin.
Tr. Francis Pott, 1861

Giovanni P. da Palestrina, 1591
Adapted W. H. Monk, 1861

Al - le - lu - ia! Al - le - lu - ia! Al - le - lu - ia!

1. The strife is o'er, the bat - tle done; The vic - to - ry of life is won;
2. The powers of death have done their worst, But Christ their le - gions hath dis-persed;
3. The three sad days are quick - ly sped; He ris - es glo - rious from the dead;
4. Lord, by the stripes which wounded Thee, From death's dread sting Thy servants free,

The song of tri - umph has be - gun. Al - le - lu - ia!
Let shouts of ho - ly joy out - burst, Al - le - lu - ia!
All glo - ry to our ris - en Head Al - le - lu - ia!
That we may live and sing to Thee, Al - le - lu - ia! A - men.

40 Crown Him With Many Crowns

DIADEMATA. S. M. D.

Matthew Bridges, 1848
Descant with stanza 4

George J. Elvey, 1868
Descant by Donald D. Kettring, 1940

Crown Him Lord, En - throned in worlds a - bove;

1. Crown Him with man - y crowns, The Lamb up - on His throne;
2. Crown Him the Son of God Be - fore the worlds be - gan,
3. Crown Him the Lord of life Who tri - umphed o'er the grave,
4. Crown Him the Lord of heav'n, En - throned in worlds a - bove;

Crown Him Lord The won-drous name of love.

Hark! how the heav'n - ly an - them drowns All mu - sic but its own:
And ye, who trod where He hath trod, Crown Him the Son of man;
And rose vic - to - rious in the strife For those He came to save;
Crown Him the King, to whom is giv'n, The won-drous name of Love.

Crown Him Lord, Crown Him Lord,

A - wake, my soul, and sing Of Him who died for thee,
Who ev - 'ry grief hath known That wrings the hu - man breast,
His glo - ries now we sing Who died, and rose on high,
Crown Him with man - y crowns, As thrones be - fore Him fall,

Crown Him Lord and King of all. A-men.

And hail Him as thy match-less King Thru all e - ter - ni - ty.
And takes and bears them for His own, That all in Him may rest.
Who died, e - ter - nal life to bring, And lives that death may die.
Crown Him, ye kings, with man - y crowns For He is King of all. A - men.

Descant copyrighted. Used by permission of the Composer.

41 Rejoice, the Lord Is King

ARTHUR'S SEAT. 6. 6. 6. 6. 8. 8. with Refrain.

Charles Wesley, 1746

John Goss, 1874

1. Re - joice, the Lord is King: Your Lord and King a - dore; Re - joice, give
2. Je - sus, the Sav - iour, reigns, The God of truth and love; When He had
3. His King-dom can - not fail, He rules o'er earth and heav'n; The keys of
4. He sits at God's right hand Till all His foes sub - mit, And bow to

Refrain

thanks and sing, And tri - umph ev - er - more;
purged our stains, He took His seat a - bove: Lift up your heart, lift
death and hell Are to our Je - sus given:
His com - mand, And fall be-neath His feet:

up your voice; Re - joice, a - gain I say, re - joice! A-men.

42 All Hail the Power of Jesus' Name!

CORONATION. C. M.

Edward Perronet, 1779
Trumpet Fanfare with Stanzas 3 and 4

Oliver Holden, 1793
Descant and Trumpet Fanfare by David Mc K. Williams, 1935

Descant with stanzas 2 and 4

1. All hail the power of Je - sus' name! Let
2. Sin - ners, whose love can ne'er for - get The
3. Let ev - ery kin - dred, ev - ery tribe, On
4. O that with yon - der sa - cred throng We

2.-4. Crown Him, Crown Je - sus Lord

an - gels pros - trate fall; Bring forth the roy - al di - a - dem,
worm-wood and the gall, Go, spread your tro - phies at His feet,
this ter - res - trial ball, To Him all maj - es - ty as - cribe,
at His feet may fall! We'll join the ev - er - last - ing song,

of all Crown Him the Lord of all.

2. Go spread your
4. We'll join the

And crown Him Lord of all; Bring forth the roy - al
And crown Him Lord of all; Go, spread your tro - phies
And crown Him Lord of all; To Him all maj - es -
And crown Him Lord of all; We'll join the ev - er -

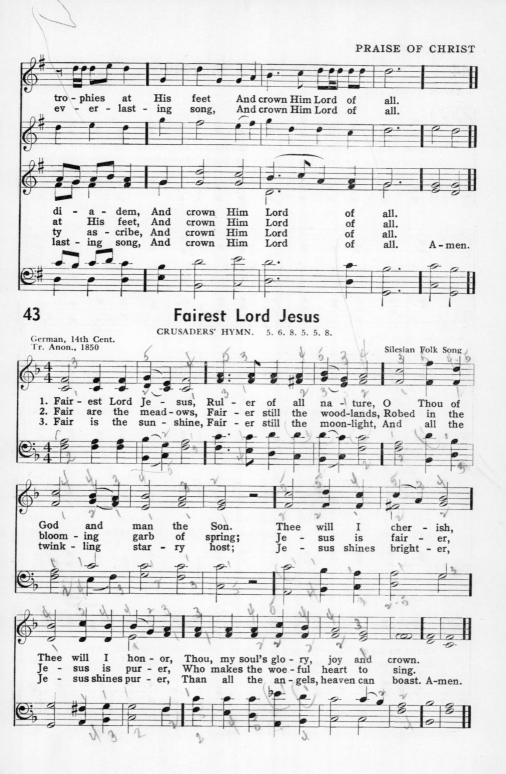

tro - phies at His feet And crown Him Lord of all.
ev - er - last - ing song, And crown Him Lord of all.

di - a - dem, And crown Him Lord of all.
at His feet, And crown Him Lord of all.
ty as - cribe, And crown Him Lord of all.
last - ing song, And crown Him Lord of all. A - men.

43   Fairest Lord Jesus

CRUSADERS' HYMN. 5. 6. 8. 5. 5. 8.

German, 14th Cent.
Tr. Anon., 1850

Silesian Folk Song

1. Fair - est Lord Je - sus, Rul - er of all na - ture, O Thou of
2. Fair are the mead - ows, Fair - er still the wood-lands, Robed in the
3. Fair is the sun - shine, Fair - er still the moon-light, And all the

God and man the Son. Thee will I cher - ish,
bloom - ing garb of spring; Je - sus is fair - er,
twink - ling star - ry host; Je - sus shines bright - er,

Thee will I hon - or, Thou, my soul's glo - ry, joy and crown.
Je - sus is pur - er, Who makes the woe - ful heart to sing.
Je - sus shines pur - er, Than all the an - gels, heaven can boast. A-men.

44 Christ Walks in Beauty

Thomas Tiplady, 1944   Traditional Melody

1. From Naz - a - reth the Lord has come, And walks in Gal - i - lee
2. From Gal - i - lee, the Ris - en Lord Now comes to eve - ry land,

A - long the nar - row, crowd-ed streets, And by the tide - less sea.
To share His love with eve - ry race And lead it by the hand;

The peo - ple throng to hear His words Of sweet, ce - les - tial grace;
No more in dark-ness shall men grope, For He their light shall be;

And by the joy He leaves be - hind, His path-way all may trace.
And, from the bonds of sin and fear, The truth shall make them free.

Refrain

Christ walks in beau-ty, grace and power A-long life's com-mon ways,
And, like the dawn in sum-mer-time, A-wakes the voice of praise.

45 Thou True Vine, That Heals

PLEADING SAVIOR. 8. 7. 8. 7. D.

T. S. N. in "Songs of Praise"

Plymouth Collection, 1855

1. Thou true Vine, that heals the na-tions, Tree of life, Thy branch-es we.
2. Noth-ing can we do with-out Thee; On Thy life de-pends each one;

They who leave Thee fade and with-er, None bear fruit ex-cept in Thee.
If we keep Thy words and love Thee, All we ask for shall be done.

Cleanse us, make us sane and sim-ple, Till we merge our lives in Thine,
May we, lov-ing one an-oth-er, Ra-diant in Thy light a-bide;

Gain our-selves in Thee, the Vint-age, Give our-selves through Thee, the Vine.
So through us, made fruit-ful by Thee, Shall our God be glo-ri-fied. A-men.

Words, from "Enlarged Songs of Praise," by permission of the Oxford University Press.

46 What a Friend We Have in Jesus

ERIE. 8. 7. 8. 7. D.

Joseph Scriven, 1855

Charles C. Converse, 1868

1. What a friend we have in Je - sus, All our sins and griefs to bear;
2. Have we tri - als and temp-ta - tions? Is there trou-ble an - y - where?
3. Are we weak and heav-y - la - den, Cum-bered with a load of care?

What a priv - i - lege to car - ry Ev - 'ry-thing to God in pray'r!
We should nev - er be dis - cour - aged: Take it to the Lord in pray'r!
Pre - cious Sav-iour, still our ref - uge, Take it to the Lord in pray'r!

O what peace we oft - en for - feit, O what need-less pain we bear,
Can we find a friend so faith - ful, Who will all our sor-rows share?
Do thy friends de - spise, for-sake thee? Take it to the Lord in pray'r!

All be-cause we do not car - ry Ev - 'ry-thing to God in pray'r.
Je - sus knows our ev - 'ry weak-ness— Take it to the Lord in pray'r!
In His arms He'll take and shield thee, Thou wilt find a sol-ace there. A-men.

47 In Our Work and in Our Play

ROSSLYN. 7. 7. 7. 7. 7. 7.

Whitfield G. Wills, 1841-1891

English Melody

1. In our work and in our play, Je - sus, ev - er
2. May we in Thy strength sub - due E - vil tem - pers,
3. Chil - dren of the King are we! May we loy - al

with us stay; May we al - ways strive to be
words un - true, Thoughts im - pure, and deeds un - kind,
to Him be; Try to please Him ev - 'ry day,

True and faith - ful un - to Thee. Then we truth - ful -
All things hate - ful to Thy mind. Then we truth - ful -
In our work and in our play. Then we truth - ful -

ly can sing, We are chil - dren of the King.
ly can sing, We are chil - dren of the King.
ly can sing, We are chil - dren of the King. A-men.

48 Take My Life and Let It Be

HENDON. 7. 7. 7. 7.

Frances R. Havergal, 1874

Henri A. C. Malan, 1827

1. Take my life and let it be Con - se - crat - ed, Lord, to Thee; Take my mo - ments and my days; Let them flow in cease - less praise. Let them flow in cease - less praise.
2. Take my hands, and let them move At the im - pulse of Thy love. Take my feet, and let them be Swift and beau - ti - ful for Thee. Swift and beau - ti - ful for Thee.
3. Take my voice, and let me sing, Al - ways, on - ly, for my King. Take my lips, and let them be Filled with mes - sa - ges from Thee. Filled with mes - sa - ges from Thee.
4. Take my sil - ver and my gold; Not a mite would I with-hold. Take my in - tel - lect and use Ev - ery power as Thou shalt choose, Ev - ery power as Thou shalt choose. A-men.

5 Take my will and make it Thine,
It shall be no longer mine:
Take my heart, it is Thine own,
It shall be Thy royal throne.

6 Take my love; my Lord, I pour
At Thy feet its treasure store;
Take myself, and I will be
Ever, only, all for Thee.

49

I Feel the Winds of God Today

HARDY NORSEMAN. C. M. D.

Jessie Adams, 1863

Anonymous
Norse Melody

1. I feel the winds of God to-day; To - day my sail I lift,
2. It is the wind of God that dries My vain re-gret - ful tears,
3. If ev - er I for - get Thy love And how that love was shown,

Though heav - y oft with drench - ing spray, And torn with man - y a rift;
Un - til with brav - er thoughts shall rise The pur - er, bright-er years;
Lift high the blood - red flag a - bove: It bears Thy name a - lone.

If hope but light the wa - ter's crest And Christ my barque will use,
If cast on shore of self - ish ease Or pleas - ure I should be,
Great Pi - lot of my on - ward way, Thou wilt not let me drift;

I'll seek the seas at His be - hest, And brave an - oth - er cruise.
Lord, let me feel Thy fresh-'ning breeze, And I'll put back to sea.
I feel the winds of God to - day, To - day my sail I lift.

50 Lead on, O King Eternal

LANCASHIRE 7. 6. 7. 6. D.

Ernest W. Shurtleff, 1888   Henry Smart, 1836

1. Lead on, O King E-ter-nal, The day of march has come;
2. Lead on, O King E-ter-nal, Till sin's fierce war shall cease,
3. Lead on, O King E-ter-nal, We fol-low, not with fears,

Hence-forth in fields of con-quest Thy tents shall be our home:
And ho-li-ness shall whis-per The sweet A-men of peace;
For glad-ness breaks like morn-ing Wher-e'er Thy face ap-pears:

Through days of prep-a-ra-tion Thy grace has made us strong,
For not with swords, loud clash-ing, Nor roll of stir-ring drums,
Thy Cross is lift-ed o'er us; We jour-ney in its light;

And now, O King E-ter-nal, We lift our bat-tle song.
With deeds of love and mer-cy, The heaven-ly king-dom comes.
The crown a-waits the con-quest; Lead on, O God of might. A-men.

51 Now in the Days of Youth

DIADEMATA. S. M. D.

Walter J. Mathams, 1913

George J. Elvey, 1868

1. Now in the days of youth, When life flows fresh and free, Thou Lord of all our hearts and lives, We give our-selves to Thee; Our fer - vent gift re - ceive, And fit us to ful - fill, Through all our days, in all our ways, Our heaven-ly Fa-ther's will.

2. Teach us wher - e'er we live, To act as in Thy sight, And do what Thou wouldst have us do With ra - di - ant de - light; Not choos - ing what is great, Nor spurn - ing what is small, But tak - ing from Thy hands our tasks To glo - ri - fy them all.

3. Teach us to love the true, The beau - ti - ful and pure, And let us not for one short hour An e - vil thought en - dure. But give us grace to stand De - cid - ed, brave, and strong, The lov - ers of all ho - ly things, The foes of all things wrong.

4. Spir - it of Christ, do Thou Our first bright days in - spire, That we may live the life of love And loft - i - est de - sire; And be by Thee pre - pared For larg - er years to come; And for the life in - ef - fa - ble, With - in the Fa-ther's home. A-men.

52   That Cause Can Neither Be Lost Nor Stayed

GOD'S PLAN.   9. 9. 10. 10.

Kristian C. Ostergaard, 1855-1931
Tr. by J. A. Aaberg, b. 1877

Danish Folk Tune
Harm. by Lawrence Curry

1. That cause can nei - ther be lost nor stayed
2. Each no - ble serv - ice that men have wrought
3. There - by it - self like a tree it shows:
4. Be then no more by a storm dis - mayed,

Which takes the course of what God has made,
Was first con - ceived as a fruit - ful thought;
That high it reach - es, as deep it grows;
For by it the full - grown seeds are laid;

And is not trust - ing in walls and tow - ers,
Each wor - thy cause with a fu - ture glo - rious
And when the storms are its branch - es shak - ing,
And though the tree by its might it shat - ters,

But slow - ly grow - ing from seeds to flow - ers.
By qui - et grow - ing be - comes vic - to - rious.
It deep - er root in the soil is tak - ing.
What then, if thou - sands of seeds it scat - ters?

53 God of the Prairies

MAGDA. 10. 10. 10. 10.

Cyril C. Richardson, 1938

R. Vaughan Williams, 1872

1. God of the prai - ries, by Thy bound - less grace,
2. Here shall Thy seed fall on no un - tilled soil,
3. Teach us to seek our hap - pi - ness in Thee,
4. Grant us such breadth of vi - sion that our eyes,
5. God of the prai - ries, by Thy bound - less grace,

Give us the strength to build a wor - thy race,
For we have pledged un - weary - ing hands to toil,
To know the joys of sim - ple pur - i - ty:
Scan - ning the wheat that meets the flam - ing skies
Give us the strength to build a wor - thy race,

That shall not lose its stead - fast faith in Thee, Through
Till through the miles of myr - iad wheat is heard The
Clean laugh-ter's ring and all the am - ple wealth Of
Far in the West, may nev - er be made blind Through
That shall not lose its stead - fast faith in Thee, Through

all the winds and hails of des - ti - ny.
whis - pering voice of Thine Al - might - y Word.
youth - ful strength and vig - orous life and health.
self - ish aims or nar - row - ness of mind.
all the winds and hails of des - ti - ny. A - men.

Music from "Enlarged Songs of Praise," by permission of Oxford University Press.

54 Breathe on Me, Breath of God

TRENTHAM. S. M.

Edwin Hatch, 1886   Robert Jackson, 1894

1. Breathe on me, Breath of God, Fill me with life a - new, That I may
2. Breathe on me, Breath of God, Un - til my heart is pure, Un - til with
3. Breathe on me, Breath of God, Till I am whol - ly Thine, Till all this
4. Breathe on me, Breath of God, So shall I nev - er die, But live with

love what Thou dost love, And do what Thou wouldst do.
Thee I will one will, To do or to en - dure.
earth - ly part of me Glows with Thy fire di - vine.
Thee the per - fect life Of Thine e - ter - ni - ty. A - men.

55 Holy Spirit, Truth Divine

MERCY. 7. 7. 7. 7.

Samuel Longfellow, 1864   Arr. from Louis M. Gottschalk, 1867

1. Ho - ly Spir - it, Truth di - vine, Dawn up - on this soul of mine;
2. Ho - ly Spir - it, Love di - vine, Glow with - in this heart of mine;
3. Ho - ly Spir - it, Power di - vine, Fill and nerve this will of mine;
4. Ho - ly Spir - it, Right di - vine, King with - in my con-science reign;

Word of God, and in - ward Light, Wake my spir - it, clear my sight.
Kin - dle ev - 'ry high de - sire; Per - ish self in Thy pure fire.
By Thee may I strong-ly live, Brave-ly bear, and no - bly strive.
Be my law, and I shall be Firm - ly bound, for-ev - er free. A-men.

56 Spirit of God, Descend Upon My Heart

MORECAMBE. 10. 10. 10. 10.

George Croly, 1780-1860

Frederick C. Atkinson, 1841-1897

1. Spir - it of God, de - scend up - on my heart;
2. I ask no dream, no proph - et ec - sta - sies,
3. Hast Thou not bid us love Thee, God and King?
4. Teach me to feel that Thou art al - ways nigh;
5. Teach me to love Thee as Thine an - gels love,

Wean it from earth; through all its puls - es move;
No sud - den rend - ing of the veil of clay,
All, all Thine own, soul, heart and strength and mind;
Teach me the strug - gles of the soul to bear,
One ho - ly pas - sion fill - ing all my frame;

Stoop to my weak - ness, might - y as Thou art,
No an - gel vis - i - tant, no o - pening skies;
I see Thy cross— there teach my heart to cling.
To check the ris - ing doubt, the reb - el sigh;
The bap - tism of the heaven - de - scend - ed Dove,

And make me love Thee as I ought to love.
But take the dim - ness of my soul a - way.
O let me seek Thee, and O let me find.
Teach me the pa - tience of un - an - swered prayer.
My heart an al - tar, and Thy love the flame. A-men.

57 Glorious Things of Thee Are Spoken

AUSTRIAN HYMN. 8. 7. 8. 7. D.

John Newton, 1779
Descant with stanzas 2 and 4

Joseph Haydn, 1797
Descant by I. H. Ingham, 1925

1. Glo - rious things of thee are spo-ken, Zi - on, cit - y of our God;
2. See, the streams of liv - ing wa-ters, Springing from e - ter - nal love,
3. Round each hab - i - ta - tion hov-'ring, See the cloud and fire ap-pear
4. Sav - iour, if of Zi - on's cit - y I, through grace, a mem - ber am,

He whose word can - not be bro - ken Formed thee for His own a - bode:
Well sup - ply thy sons and daugh-ters, And all fear of want re-move:
For a glo - ry and a cov-'ring Show-ing that the Lord is near:
Let the world de - ride or pit - y, I will glo - ry in Thy name:

On the Rock of A - ges found-ed, What can shake thy sure re-pose?
Who can faint, when such a riv - er Ev - er will their thirst as-suage?
Thus de - riv - ing from their ban-ner Light by night, and shade by day;
Fad - ing is the world-ling's pleasure, All his boast - ed pomp and show;

With   sal - va-tion's walls   sur - rounded,   Thou   mayst smile at   all   Thy foes.
Grace, which, like the Lord   the   Giv-er,   Nev - er   fails from age   to   age?
Safe   they feed up - on   the   man-na   Which He   gives them when they pray.
Sol - id joys and last - ing   treasure   None   but   Zi - on's chil-dren know. A-men.

Descant by I. H. Ingham, 1925.   Used by permission.

58   Faith of Our Fathers, Living Still

ST. CATHERINE.   L. M.   with Refrain

Frederick W. Faber, 1849   Henry F. Hemy and J. G. Walton, 1874

1. Faith of our fa - thers, liv - ing still   In spite of dun-geon, fire   and sword,
2. Faith of our fa - thers, we   will strive   To win all   na-tions un - to Thee;
3. Faith of our fa - thers, we   will love   Both friend and foe   in   all   our strife,

O   how our   hearts beat high with joy   When-e'er we hear that   glo - rious word!
And through the truth that   comes from God   Man-kind shall then in - deed be free.
And preach Thee, too, as   love knows how   By   kind-ly words and   vir - tuous life.

Refrain

Faith of our fa - thers, ho - ly faith,   We will be true to Thee till death. A-men.

59 The Church's One Foundation

AURELIA. 7. 6. 7. 6. D.

Samuel J. Stone, 1866   Samuel S. Wesley, 1864

1. The Church's one foun-da-tion Is Je-sus Christ her Lord;
2. E-lect from ev-'ry na-tion Yet one o'er all the earth,
3. Though with a scorn-ful won-der Men see her sore op-pressed,

She is His new cre-a-tion By wa-ter and the word:
Her char-ter of sal-va-tion One Lord, one faith, one birth;
By schisms rent a-sun-der, By her-e-sies dis-tressed,

From heav'n He came and sought her To be His ho-ly bride;
One ho-ly name she bless-es, Par-takes one ho-ly food!
Yet saints their watch are keep-ing, Their cry goes up, "How long?"

With His own blood He bought her, And for her life He died.
And to one hope she press-es, With ev-'ry grace en-dued.
And soon the night of weep-ing Shall be the morn of song. A-men.

4 'Mid toil and tribulation,
   And tumult of her war,
She waits the consummation
   Of peace for evermore;
Till with the vision glorious
   Her longing eyes are blest,
And the great Church victorious
   Shall be the Church at rest.

5 Yet she on earth hath union
   With God the Three in One,
And mystic sweet communion
   With those whose rest is won:
O happy ones and holy!
   Lord, give us grace that we,
Like them the meek and lowly,
   On high may dwell with Thee.

60 Hope of the World

ANCIENT OF DAYS (Albany). 11. 10. 11. 10.

Georgia Harkness, 1953

J. Albert Jeffery, 1886

1. Hope of the world, Thou Christ of great com-pas - sion,
2. Hope of the world, God's gift from high-est heav - en,
3. Hope of the world, a - foot on dust - y high-ways,
4. Hope of the world, who by Thy cross didst save us

Speak to our fear - ful hearts by con - flict rent. Save us, Thy peo - ple,
Bring - ing to hun - gry souls the bread of life, Still let Thy spir - it
Show - ing to wan-dering souls the path of light; Walk Thou be - side us
From death and dark de - spair, from sin and guilt; We ren-der back the

from con-sum-ing pas - sion, Who by our own false hopes and aims are spent.
un - to us be giv - en To heal earth's wounds and end her bit - ter strife.
lest the tempt-ing by - ways Lure us a - way from Thee to end - less night.
love Thy mer-cy gave us; Take Thou our lives and use them as Thou wilt. A-men.

5 Hope of the world, O Christ, o'er death victorious,
Who by this sign didst conquer grief and pain,
We would be faithful to Thy gospel glorious:
Thou art our Lord; Thou dost forever reign!

61 As Drops the Gentle Rain from Heaven

BRATTON. C. M. D.

S. Baring-Gould

A Basque Air

1. As drops the gen - tle rain from Heaven As falls the glis - 'ning snow,
2. And lo! where earth was cold and bare, A fruit - ful har - vest grows;
3. The Word from out the mouth of God Shall sound through ev - 'ry clime,

And wa - ters all the wea - ry land, And makes the herb - age grow,
The des - ert puts its man - tle on, And blos-soms as the rose;
And void to Him shall ne'er re - turn, Nor fail at an - y time.

So com - eth down the Word of God, On spir - its faint and dry,
Where once the cru - el thorn bush spread, The fir tree now is seen,
Then thank we Him who gave the Word A light to feet that stray,

On hearts where all is bar - ren - ness, On souls that sleep-ing lie.
Where grew a - pace the worth-less brier, Ap - pears the myr - tle green.
A heal - ing balm for sick-ened souls For fal-tering steps a stay.

62 **Break Thou the Bread of Life**

BREAD OF LIFE. 6. 4. 6. 4. D.

Mary Ann Lathbury, 1841-1913

William F. Sherwin, 1826-1888

1. Break Thou the bread of life, Dear Lord, to me,
2. Bless Thou the truth, dear Lord, Now un - to me—

As Thou didst break the loaves Be - side the sea;
As Thou didst bless the bread By Gal - i - lee;

Be - yond the sa - cred page I seek Thee, Lord;
Then shall all bond - age cease, All fet - ters fall;

My spir - it pants for Thee, O liv - ing Word.
And I shall find my peace, My All in all. A - men.

63 Thy Word Is Like a Garden, Lord

FOREST GREEN. C. M. D.

Edwin Hodder, 1868

English traditional melody
Arr. by R. Vaughan Williams, 1906

1. Thy Word is like a gar - den, Lord, With flow - ers bright and fair;
2. Thy Word is like a star - ry host: A thou - sand rays of light

And ev - ery one who seeks may pluck A love - ly clus - ter there.
Are seen to guide the trav - el - er And make his path - way bright.

Thy Word is like a deep, deep mine; And jew - els rich and rare
O may I love Thy pre - cious Word, May I ex - plore the mine,

Are hid - den in its might - y depths For ev - ery search - er there.
May I its fra - grant flow-ers glean, May light up - on me shine. A-men.

O Word of God Incarnate

64

MUNICH. 7. 6. 7. 6. D.

William D. How, 1823-1897

"Neuvermehrtes Meiningisches Gesangbuch," 1693
Arr. by Felix Mendelssohn-Bartholdy, 1809-1847

1. O Word of God In-car-nate, O Wis-dom from on high,
2. The Church from Thee, her Mas-ter, Re-ceived the gift di-vine,
3. It float-eth like a ban-ner Be-fore God's host un-furled;
4. O make Thy Church, dear Sav-iour, A lamp of pur-est gold,

O Truth un-changed, un-chang-ing, O Light of our dark sky:
And still that light she lift-eth O'er all the earth to shine.
It shin-eth like a bea-con A-bove the dark-ling world.
To bear be-fore the na-tions Thy true light, as of old.

We praise Thee for the ra-diance That from the hal-lowed page,
It is the sa-cred cas-ket, Where gems of truth are stored;
It is the chart and com-pass That o'er life's surg-ing sea,
O teach Thy wan-d'ring pil-grims By this their path to trace,

A lan-tern to our foot-steps, Shines on from age to age.
It is the heav'n-drawn pic-ture Of Thee, the liv-ing Word.
'Mid mists and rocks and quick-sands, Still guides, O Christ, to Thee.
Till, clouds and dark-ness end-ed, They see Thee face to face. A-men.

65 This Is My Father's World

TERRA BEATA. S. M. D.

Maltbie D. Babcock, 1901

Franklin L. Sheppard, 1915

1. This is my Fa-ther's world, And to my lis-tening ears, All na-ture sings, and round me rings The mu-sic of the spheres. This is my Fa-ther's world: I rest me in the thought Of rocks and trees, of skies and seas; His hand the won-ders wrought.

2. This is my Fa-ther's world, The birds their car-ols raise, The morn-ing light, the lil-y white, De-clare their Mak-er's praise. This is my Fa-ther's world: He shines in all that's fair; In the rus-tling grass I hear Him pass, He speaks to me ev-ery-where.

3. This is my Fa-ther's world, O let me ne'er for-get That though the wrong seems oft so strong, God is the Rul-er yet. This is my Fa-ther's world: The bat-tle is not done; Je-sus who died shall be sat-is-fied, And earth and heaven be one. A-men.

66 All Things Bright and Beautiful

GREYSTONE. 6. 7. 6. 7. D. with Refrain.

Cecil Frances Alexander, 1848

W. R. Waghorne, 1906

Refrain

1. All things bright and beau - ti - ful, All crea - tures great and small,

All things wise and won - der - ful, The Lord God made them all. A - men.

Fine

The remaining verses begin here.

2. Each lit - tle flower that o - pens, Each lit - tle bird that sings,
3. The pur - ple head - ed moun - tain, The riv - er run - ning by,
4. The cold wind in the win - ter, The pleas - ant sum - mer sun,
5. The tall trees in the green - wood, The mead - ows where we play,
6. He gave us eyes to see them, And lips that we might tell

D. C.

He made their glow - ing col - ors, He made their ti - ny wings.
The sun - set, and the morn - ing That bright - ens up the sky,
The ripe fruits in the gar - den, He made them ev - 'ry one.
The rush - es by the wa - ter, We gath - er ev - 'ry day,
How great is God Al - might - y, Who has made all things well.

67 The Spacious Firmament on High

CREATION. L. M. D.

Joseph Addison, 1712

From The Creation
Franz J. Haydn, 1795

1. The spa-cious fir-ma-ment on high, With all the blue e-the-real sky, And span-gled heav'ns a shin-ing frame, Their great O-rig-i-nal pro-claim. Th'un-wea-ried sun, from day to day, Does his Cre-a-tor's power dis-play, And pub-lish-es, to

2. Soon as the eve-ning shades pre-vail, The moon takes up the won-drous tale; And night-ly, to the list-'ning earth, Re-peats the sto-ry of her birth; Whilst all the stars that round her burn, And all the plan-ets in their turn, Con-firm the ti-dings,

3. What though, in sol-emn si-lence, all Move round the dark ter-res-trial ball? What tho' no real voice, nor sound, A-midst their ra-diant orbs be found? In rea-son's ear they all re-joice, And ut-ter forth a glo-rious voice; For ev-er sing-ing,

Ped.

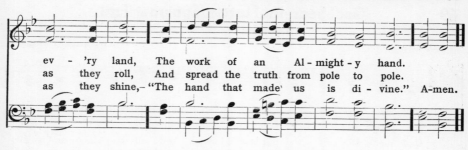

ev - 'ry land, The work of an Al - might - y hand.
as they roll, And spread the truth from pole to pole.
as they shine,— "The hand that made us is di - vine." A-men.

68   For the Beauty of the Earth

DIX. 7. 7. 7. 7. 7. 7.

Folliott S. Pierpoint, 1864

Abridged from a chorale
by Conrad Kocher, 1838

1. For the beau - ty of the earth, For the glo - ry of the skies,
2. For the beau - ty of each hour Of the day and of the night,
3. For the joy of hu - man love, Broth-er, sis - ter, par - ent, child,

For the love which from our birth O - ver and a - round us lies:
Hill and vale, and tree and flower, Sun and moon, and stars of light:
Friends on earth, and friends a - bove; For all gen - tle thoughts and mild:

Lord of all, to Thee we raise This our hymn of grate - ful praise. A-men.

4 For Thy Church, that evermore
   Lifteth holy hands above,
Offering up on every shore
   Her pure sacrifice of love:
Lord of all, to Thee we raise
This our hymn of grateful praise.

5 For Thyself, best Gift Divine!
   To our race so freely given;
For that great, great love of Thine,
   Peace on earth, and joy in heaven:
Lord of all, to Thee we raise
This our hymn of grateful praise.

69 God Sees the Little Sparrow Fall

PROVIDENCE. C. M. with Refrain.

Maria Straub, 1838-1898

S. W. Straub, 1842-1899

1. God sees the lit - tle spar - row fall, It meets His ten - der view;
2. He paints the lil - y of the field, Per-fumes each lil - y bell;
3. God made the lit - tle birds and flowers, And all things large and small;

If God so loves the lit - tle birds, I know He loves me too.
If He so loves the lit - tle flowers, I know He loves me well.
He'll not for - get His lit - tle ones, I know He loves them all.

Refrain

He loves me too, He loves me too, I know He loves me too;

Be - cause He loves the lit - tle things, I know He loves me too. A-men.

70   Can You Count the Stars?

8. 6. 8. 7. 8. 8. 7. 7.

Wilhelm Hey, 1789-1854
Tr. H. W. Dulcken, vv. 1, 3
v. 2, anon.

German Folk Tune

1. Can you count the stars that bright-ly Twin-kle in the mid - night sky?
2. Can you count the wings now flash-ing In the sun-shines gold-en light?
3. Do you know how man - y chil - dren Rise each morn-ing blithe and gay?

Can you count the clouds, so light - ly O'er the mead-ows float-ing by?
Can you count the fish - es splash-ing In the cool - ing wa - ters bright?
Can you count their jol - ly voic - es, Sing-ing sweet-ly day by day?

God, the Lord, doth mark their num-ber With His eyes that nev - er slum-ber;
God, the Lord, a name hath giv - en, To all crea-tures un - der heav-en;
God hears all the hap - py voic - es, In their mer - ry songs re - joic - es;

He hath made them ev - 'ry one, He hath made them ev - 'ry one.
He hath named them ev - 'ry one, He hath named them ev - 'ry one.
And He loves them, ev - 'ry one, And He loves them, ev - 'ry one.

1 Weisst du, wie viel Sternlein stehen an dem blauen Himmelszelt?
Weisst du, wie viel Wolken gehen weithin über alle Welt?
Gott der Herr hat sie gezählet, dass ihm auch nicht eines fehlet
An der ganzen grossen Zahl, an der ganzen grossen Zahl.

2 Weisst du, wieviel Mücklein spielen in der hellen Sonnenglut,
Wieviel Fischlein auch sich kühlen in der hellen Wasserflut?
Gott der Herr rief sie mit Namen, dass sie all ins Leben kamen,
Dass sie nun so fröhlich sind, dass sie nun so fröhlich sind.

3 Weisst du, wievel Kinder frühe stehn aus ihrem Bettlein auf,
Dass sie ohne Sorg und Mühe fröhlich sind im Tageslauf?
Gott im Himmel hat an allen seine Lust, sein Wohlgefallen,
Kennt auch dich und hat dich lieb, kennt auch dich und hat dich lieb.

71 Father, We Thank Thee for the Night

ONSLOW. 8. 8. 8. 8.

Rebecca J. Weston, c. 1890

D. Batchellor

1. Fa - ther, we thank Thee for the night, And for the pleas-ant morn-ing light;
2. Help us to do the things we should, To be to oth - ers kind and good;

For rest and food and lov - ing care, And all that makes the world so fair.
In all we do, in work or play, To love Thee bet - ter day by day. A-men.

Used by permission of the Oliver Ditson Company.

72 Saviour, Teach Me, Day by Day

POSEN. 7. 7. 7. 7.

Jane E. Leeson, 1842

Georg C. Strattner, 1691

1. Sav - iour, teach me, day by day, Love's sweet les - son, to o - bey;
2. With a child's glad heart of love, At Thy bid - ding may I move,
3. Teach me thus Thy steps to trace, Strong to fol - low in Thy grace,
4. Love in lov - ing finds em - ploy, In o - be-dience all her joy;

Sweet - er les - son can-not be, Lov - ing Him who first loved me.
Prompt to serve and fol - low Thee, Lov - ing Him who first loved me.
Learn - ing how to love from Thee, Lov - ing Him who first loved me.
Ev - er new that joy will be, Lov - ing Him who first loved me. A-men.

73 Take Thou My Hand, O Father

SO NIMM DENN MEINE HÄNDE. 7. 4. 7. 4. D.

Julie von Haussmann, 1825-1901
Tr. H. J. L., 1954

Friedrich Silcher, 1789-1860

1. Take Thou my hand, O Fa-ther, And lead me on; Un-til my jour-ney end-eth, And life is done. With-out Thy faith-ful pres-ence I go a-stray; Be Thou my guide and com-fort, On all the way.

2. O heal Thou in Thy mer-cy My wound-ed heart. In pain and sor-row, take me With Thee, a-part, And at Thy feet re-clin-ing Teach me the way Of child-like trust and du-ty Till end of day.

3. E'en though I may not feel, Lord, Thy power and might, Yet Thou dost ne'er for-sake me Through darkest night. So take my hand, O Fa-ther, And lead me on Un-til my jour-ney end-eth And life is done. A-men.

1 So nimm denn meine Hände
Unde führe mich
Bis on mein selig Ende
Und ewiglich!
Ich kann allein nicht gehen
Nicht einen Schritt;
Wo du wirst geh'n und stehen,
Da nimm mich mit.

2 In deine Gnade hülle
Mein schwaches Herz,
Und mach' es endlich stille
In Freud' und Schmerz;
Lass ruh'n zu Deinen Füssen
Dein schwaches Kind,
Es will die Augen schliessen
Und folgen blind.

3 Wenn ich auch gar nichts fühle
Von deiner Macht,
Du bringst mich durch zum Ziele
Auch durch die Nacht;
So nimm denn meine Hände
Und führe mich
Bis an mein selig' Ende
Und ewiglich!

74 Pray When the Morn Is Breaking

MEIRIONYDD. 7. 6. 7. 6. D.

Mrs. J. C. Simpson, 1831
and others.

W. Lloyd, 1785-1852

1. Pray when the morn is break-ing, Pray when the noon is bright,
2. Re - mem - ber all who love thee, All who are loved by thee,
3. But if 'tis e'er de - nied thee In sol - i - tude to pray,

Pray with the eve's de - clin - ing, Pray in the hush of night:
And next for those that hate thee Pray thou, if such there be:
Should ho - ly thoughts come o'er thee Up - on life's crowd-ed way,

With mind made clear of tu - mult, All mean - er thoughts a - way,
Last for thy - self in meek - ness A bless - ing hum - bly claim,
E'en then the si - lent breath - ing That lifts thy soul a - bove

Make thou thy soul trans-par - ent, Seek thou with God to pray.
And link with each pe - ti - tion Thy great Re - deem-er's name.
Shall reach the thron - èd Pres - ence Of mer - cy, truth, and love. A-men.

75 Dear Lord and Father of Mankind

WHITTIER. 8. 6. 8. 8. 6.

John G. Whittier, 1872   Frederick C. Maker, 1887

1. Dear Lord and Fa - ther of man-kind, For - give our fev - 'rish ways;
2. In sim - ple trust like theirs who heard, Be - side the Syr - ian sea,
3. O Sab - bath rest by Gal - i - lee! O calm of hills a - bove,
4. With that deep hush sub - du - ing all Our words and works that drown

Re - clothe us in our right - ful mind, In pur - er lives Thy
The gra - cious call - ing of the Lord, Let us, like them, with -
Where Je - sus knelt to share with Thee The si - lence of e -
The ten - der whis - per of Thy call, As noise - less let Thy

serv - ice find, In deep - er rev - 'rence, praise.
out a word Rise up and fol - low Thee.
ter - ni - ty, In - ter - pret - ed by love!
bless - ing fall As fell Thy man - na down. A - men.

5 Drop Thy still dews of quietness,
   Till all our strivings cease:
   Take from our souls the strain and stress,
   And let our ordered lives confess
   The beauty of Thy peace.

6 Breathe through the pulses of desire
   Thy coolness and Thy balm;
   Let sense be dumb, its heats expire:
   Speak through the earthquake, wind, and fire,
   O still, small voice of calm!

Jesus, Lover of My Soul

ABERYSTWYTH. 7. 7. 7. 7. D.

Charles Wesley, 1740

Joseph Parry, 1879
Descant by Alan Gray

1. Je - sus, Lov - er of my soul, Let me to Thy bos - om fly,
2. Oth - er ref - uge have I none; Hangs my help-less soul on Thee;
3. Thou, O Christ, art all I want; More than all in Thee I find:
4. Plen - teous grace with Thee is found, Grace to cov - er all my sin;

While the near - er wa - ters roll, While the tem-pest still is high:
Leave, ah! leave me not a - lone, Still sup - port and com-fort me.
Raise the fall - en, cheer the faint, Heal the sick, and lead the blind.
Let the heal - ing streams a - bound; Make and keep me pure with - in.

Hide me, O my Sav - iour, hide, Till the storm of life is past;
All my trust on Thee is stayed, All my help from Thee I bring;
Just and ho - ly is Thy Name; I am all un - right - eous-ness;
Thou of life the Foun - tain art, Free - ly let me take of Thee;

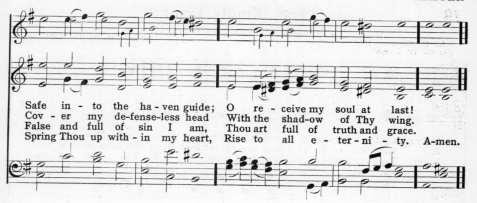

Safe in - to the ha - ven guide; O re - ceive my soul at last!
Cov - er my de-fense-less head With the shad-ow of Thy wing.
False and full of sin I am, Thou art full of truth and grace.
Spring Thou up with - in my heart, Rise to all e - ter - ni - ty. A-men.

77   Weary, Now I Close Mine Eyes

MÜDE BIN ICH GEH ZUR RUH

Luise Hensel, 1798-1876
Tr. H. J. L., 1954

German Folk Tune

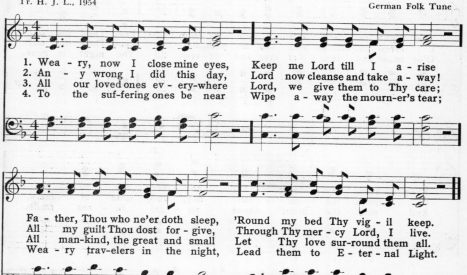

1. Wea - ry, now I close mine eyes, Keep me Lord till I a - rise
2. An - y wrong I did this day, Lord now cleanse and take a - way!
3. All our loved ones ev - ery-where Lord, we give them to Thy care;
4. To the suf-fering ones be near Wipe a - way the mourn-er's tear;

Fa - ther, Thou who ne'er doth sleep, 'Round my bed Thy vig - il keep.
All my guilt Thou dost for - give, Through Thy mer - cy Lord, I live.
All man-kind, the great and small Let Thy love sur-round them all.
Wea - ry trav-elers in the night, Lead them to E - ter - nal Light.

1 Müde bin ich, geh zur Ruh,
  Schliese meine Augen zu;
  Vater, lass die Augen dein
  Ueber meinem Bette sein.

2 Hab ich Unrecht heut' getan,
  Sieh es, treuer Gott, nicht an!
  Deine Gnad und Jesu Blut
  Macht ja allen Schaden gut.

3 Alle, die mir sind verwandt,
  Gott, lass ruhn in Deiner Hand;
  Allen Menschen, gross und klein,
  Sollen dir befohlen sein.

4 Kranken Herzen sende Ruh,
  Nasse Augen schliesse zu;
  Lass, die noch im Finstern gehn,
  Bald den Stern der Weisen sehn!

78 Lead, Kindly Light

SANDON. 10. 4. 10. 4. 10. 10.

John H. Newman, 1833
Descant (v. 3 only)

Charles H. Purday, 1799-1885

1. Lead, kind-ly Light, a - mid th' en-cir-cling gloom, Lead Thou me on;
2. I was not ev - er thus, nor prayed that Thou Shouldst lead me on;
3. So long Thy power hath blest me, sure it still Will lead me on,

The night is dark, and I am far from home; Lead Thou me on.
I loved to choose and see my path, but now Lead Thou me on;
O'er moor and fen, o'er crag and tor-rent, till The night is gone,

Keep Thou my feet; I do not ask to see
I loved the gar - ish day, and, spite of fears,
And with the morn those an - gel fa - ces smile,

The dis - tant scene,— one step e - nough for me.
Pride ruled my will. Re - mem - ber not past years.
Which I have loved long since, and lost a - while. A - men.

Descant copyright by United Church Pub. House. Used by permission.

79 Rock of Ages, Cleft for Me

TOPLADY. 7. 7. 7. 7. 7. 7.

Augustus M. Toplady, 1776
Stanza 4, Line 2, Alt. by
Thomas Cotterill, 1815

Thomas Hastings, 1830

1. Rock of A - ges, cleft for me, Let me hide my - self in Thee; Let the wa - ter and the blood, From Thy riv - en side which flowed, Be of sin the dou - ble cure, Cleanse me from its guilt and power.

2. Not the la - bors of my hands Can ful - fill Thy law's de - mands; Could my zeal no res - pite know, Could my tears for - ev - er flow, All for sin could not a - tone; Thou must save, and Thou a - lone.

3. Noth - ing in my hand I bring, Sim - ply to Thy cross I cling; Nak - ed, come to Thee for dress, Help - less, look to Thee for grace; Foul, I to the foun - tain fly; Wash me, Sav - iour, or I die.

4. While I draw this fleet - ing breath, When my eye - lids close in death, When I soar to worlds un - known, See Thee on Thy judg - ment throne, Rock of A - ges, cleft for me, Let me hide my - self in Thee. A - men.

80 Heralds of Christ

NATIONAL HYMN. 10. 10. 10. 10.

Laura S. Copenhaver, 1868-1940   George W. Warren, 1828-1902

Repeated before
stanzas 2, 3, 4

1. Her - alds of Christ, who bear the King's com-mands,
2. Through des-ert ways, dark fen, and deep mor - ass,
3. Where once the twist - ing trail in dark-ness wound
4. Lord, give us faith and strength the road to build,

Im - mor - tal ti - dings in your mor - tal hands,
Through jun - gles, slug - gish seas, and moun - tain pass,
Let march - ing feet and joy - ous song re - sound,
To see the prom - ise of the day ful - filled,

Pass on and car - ry swift the news ye bring;
Build ye the road, and fal - ter not nor stay;
Where burned the fu - neral pyres, let chil - dren sing,
When war shall be no more and strife shall cease

Make straight, make straight the high - way of the King.
Pre - pare a - cross the earth the King's high - way.
Make straight, make straight the high - way of the King.
Up - on the high - way of the Prince of Peace. A - men.

81 In Christ There Is no East or West

ST. PETER. C. M.

John Oxenham, 1908

Alexander R. Reinagle, 1836

1. In Christ there is no East or West, In Him no South or North;
2. In Him shall true hearts ev-'ry-where Their high com-mun-ion find;
3. Join hands, then, broth-ers of the faith, What-e'er your race may be.
4. In Christ now meet both East and West, In Him meet South and North;

But one great fel-low-ship of love Through-out the whole wide earth.
His serv-ice is the gold-en cord Close bind-ing all man-kind.
Who serves my Fa-ther as a son Is sure-ly kin to me.
All Christ-ly souls are one in Him Through-out the whole wide earth. A-men.

Words used by permission of the American Tract Society, copyright owners.

82 Jesus Shall Reign

DUKE STREET. L. M.

Isaac Watts, 1719

John Hatton, c. 1793

1. Je-sus shall reign wher-e'er the sun Does his suc-ces-sive journeys run;
2. To Him shall end-less prayer be made, And prais-es throng to crown His head;
3. Peo-ple and realms of ev-'ry tongue Dwell on His love with sweet-est song;
4. Bless-ings a-bound wher-e'er He reigns; The pris-oner leaps to lose his chains,
5. Let ev-'ry crea-ture rise and bring Pe-cu-liar hon-ors to our King;

His king-dom spread from shore to shore, Till moons shall wax and wane no more.
His name, like sweet per-fume, shall rise With ev-'ry morn-ing sac-ri-fice.
And in-fant voi-ces shall pro-claim Their ear-ly bless-ings on His name.
The wea-ry find e-ter-nal rest, And all the sons of want are blest.
An-gels de-scend with songs a-gain, And earth re-peat the loud A-men! A-men.

83 The Work Is Thine, O Christ

DIE SACH' IST DEIN. 8. 6. 8. 6. 8. 8. 8. 8. 8. 4. 6.

S. Preiswerk—V. 1-2.
F. Zaremba—V. 3.
Tr. J. Horstmann, 1908

Franz J. Haydn, 1732-1809

1. The work is Thine, O Christ our Lord, The cause for which we stand;
2. Thru suf-f'ring Thou, O Christ, didst go Un - to Thy throne a - bove,
3. Thou hast, O Sav - ior, led the way Thru ag - o - ny and death;

And be - ing Thine, 'twill o - ver-come Its foes on ev - 'ry hand.
And lead - est now the self-same way Those true in faith and love;
O give, we pray, yet more and more Thy Spir - it's liv - ing breath!

Yet grains of wheat, be - fore they grow, Are bur - ied in the earth be - low;
So lead us, then, tho' suf-f'rings wait, To share Thy king-dom's heav'n-ly state,
Send mes-sen - gers o'er land and sea To bring Thy chil-dren all to Thee;

All that is old doth per - ish there To form a life both new and fair:
Thy death has bro - ken Sa-tan's might, And leads the faith-ful to the light;
Thy name can save, Thy name makes free; We con - se - crate our-selves to Thee

So too are we From self and sin made free.
E - ter - nal light, From dark - ness in - to light.
As serv - ants true, As war - riors brave and true. A-men.

84 Spread, Still Spread, Thou Mighty Word

GOTT SEI DANK. 7. 7. 7. 7.

J. F. Bahnmaier, 1774-1841

"Freylinghausen's Gesangbuch," 1704

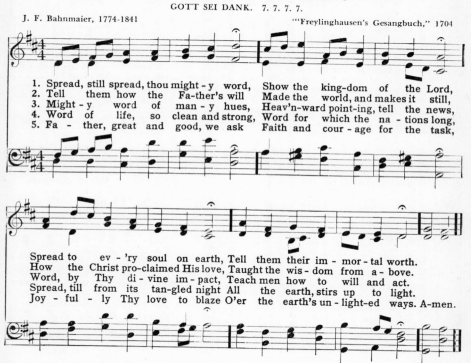

1. Spread, still spread, thou might - y word, Show the king-dom of the Lord,
2. Tell them how the Fa-ther's will Made the world, and makes it still,
3. Might - y word of man - y hues, Heav'n-ward point-ing, tell the news,
4. Word of life, so clean and strong, Word for which the na - tions long,
5. Fa - ther, great and good, we ask Faith and cour - age for the task,

Spread to ev - 'ry soul on earth, Tell them their im - mor - tal worth.
How the Christ pro-claimed His love, Taught the wis - dom from a - bove.
Word, by Thy di - vine im - pact, Teach men how to will and act.
Spread, till from its tan-gled night All the earth, stirs up to light.
Joy - ful - ly Thy love to blaze O'er the earth's un - light - ed ways. A-men.

Die Sach' ist Dein

Melody on opposite page.

1 Die Sach' ist Dein, Herr Jesu Christ,
Die Sach' an der wir steh'n,
Und weil es Deine Sache ist,
Kann sie nicht untergeh'n.
Allein das Weizenkorn, bevor
Es fruchtbar sprosst zum Licht empor,
Muss sterben in der Erde Schoss
Zuvor vom eig'nen Wesen los.
Durch Sterben los,
Vom eig'nen Wesen los.

2 Du gingst, O Jesu, unser Haupt,
Durch Leiden himmelan,
Und führest Jeden, der da glaubt,
Mit Dir die gleiche Bahn.
Wohlan, so nimm uns allzugleich
Zum Teil am Leiden und am Reich;
Führ' uns durch Deines Todes Tor
Samt Deiner Sach' zum Licht empor,
Zum Light empor,
Durch Nacht zum Light empor!

85 Where Cross the Crowded Ways of Life

GERMANY. L. M.

Frank Mason North, 1905

Melody adapted from Beethoven, 1770-1827
William Gardiner's *Sacred Melodies*, 1815

1. Where cross the crowd-ed ways of life, Where sound the cries of race and clan,
2. In haunts of wretch-ed-ness and need, On shadowed thresh-olds dark with fears,
3. From ten-der child-hood's help-less-ness, From woman's grief, man's bur-dened toil,
4. The cup of wa-ter given for Thee Still holds the fresh-ness of Thy grace;

A - bove the noise of sel - fish strife, We hear Thy voice, O Son of Man.
From paths where hide the lures of greed, We catch the vi - sion of Thy tears.
From famished souls, from sorrow's stress, Thy heart has nev-er known re-coil.
Yet long these mul - ti-tudes to see The sweet compassion of Thy face. A-men.

5 O Master, from the mountain side,
Make haste to heal these hearts of pain;
Among these restless throngs abide,
O tread the city's streets again;

6 Till sons of men shall learn Thy love,
And follow where Thy feet have trod;
Till glorious from Thy heaven above,
Shall come the City of our God.

86 O Master, Let Me Walk with Thee

Washington Gladden, 1879

MARYTON. L. M.

Henry Percy Smith, 1874

1. O Mas-ter, let me walk with Thee In low - ly paths of serv - ice free;
2. Help me the slow of heart to move By some clear, win - ning word of love;
3. Teach me Thy pa-tience; still with Thee In clos - er, dear - er com - pa - ny,
4. In hope that sends a shin - ing ray Far down the fu - ture's broadening way;

Tell me Thy se - cret; help me bear The strain of toil, the fret of care.
Teach me the way-ward feet to stay, And guide them in the home-ward way.
In work that keeps faith sweet and strong, In trust that tri-umphs o - ver wrong;
In peace that on - ly Thou canst give, With Thee, O Mas-ter, let me live. A-men.

87 O Zion, Haste

TIDINGS. 11. 10. 11. 10. with Refrain.

Mary A. Thompson, 1834-1923

James Walch, 1837-1901

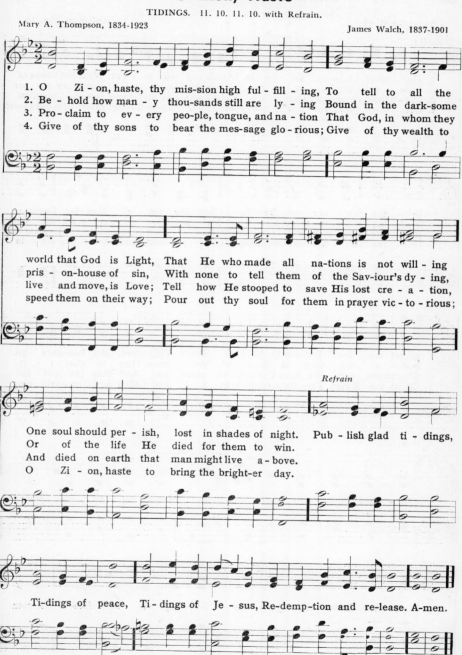

1. O Zi - on, haste, thy mis-sion high ful - fill - ing, To tell to all the
2. Be - hold how man - y thou-sands still are ly - ing Bound in the dark-some
3. Pro - claim to ev - ery peo-ple, tongue, and na - tion That God, in whom they
4. Give of thy sons to bear the mes-sage glo - rious; Give of thy wealth to

world that God is Light, That He who made all na-tions is not will - ing
pris - on-house of sin, With none to tell them of the Sav-iour's dy - ing,
live and move, is Love; Tell how He stooped to save His lost cre - a - tion,
speed them on their way; Pour out thy soul for them in prayer vic - to - rious;

Refrain

One soul should per - ish, lost in shades of night. Pub - lish glad ti - dings,
Or of the life He died for them to win.
And died on earth that man might live a - bove.
O Zi - on, haste to bring the bright-er day.

Ti-dings of peace, Ti - dings of Je - sus, Re-demp-tion and re-lease. A-men.

88 Onward, Christian Soldiers

ST. GERTRUDE. 6. 5. 6. 5. D. with Refrain.

S. Baring-Gould, 1865

Arthur Sullivan, 1871

1. On - ward, Chris-tian sol - diers, March-ing as to war, With the Cross of
2. Like a might-y ar - my Moves the Church of God; Broth-ers we are
3. Crowns and thrones may per - ish, King-doms rise and wane, But the Church of
4. On - ward, then, ye peo - ple! Join our hap-py throng! Blend with ours your

Je - sus Go - ing on be - fore; Christ the roy - al Mas - ter Leads a-
tread - ing Where the saints have trod; We are not di - vid - ed, All one
Je - sus Con - stant will re - main; Gates of hell can nev - er 'Gainst that
voi - ces In the tri-umph song; Glo - ry, laud, and hon - or, Un - to

gainst the foe; For-ward in - to bat - tle, See, His ban-ners go.
bod - y we, One in hope and doc - trine, One in char - i - ty.
Church pre - vail; We have Christ's own prom - ise, And that can-not fail.
Christ the King; This thru count-less a - ges Men and an - gels sing.

Refrain

On - ward, Chris - tian sol - diers March - ing as to war,

With the Cross of Je - sus Go - ing on be - fore. A-men.

89 Remember All the People

FAR OFF LANDS. 7. 6. 7. 6. D.

Percy Dearmer

Hymn of the Bohemian Brethren
From Hemmet's *Koral Bok*

1. Re - mem - ber all the peo - ple Who live in far off lands,
2. Some work in sul - try for - ests Where apes swing to and fro,
3. God bless the men and wo - men Who serve Him o - ver - sea;

In strange and lone - ly ci - ties, Or roam the des - ert sands,
Some fish in might - y riv - ers, Some hunt a - cross the snow.
God raise up more to help them To set the na - tions free,

Or farm the moun - tain pas - tures, Or till the end - less plains
Re - mem - ber all God's chil - dren, Who yet have nev - er heard
Till all the dis - tant peo - ple In ev - 'ry for - eign place

Where chil - dren wade through rice fields And watch the cam - el trains.
The truth that comes from Je - sus, The glo - ry of His word.
Shall un - der - stand His King - dom And come in - to His grace. A - men.

90 # God the All-merciful

RUSSIAN HYMN. 11. 10. 11. 9.

Henry F. Chorley, 1842
John Ellerton, 1870

Alex T. Lwoff, 1833

1. God the All - mer - ci - ful! earth hath for - sak - en
2. God the All - right - eous One! man hath de - fied Thee,
3. God the All - wise! by the fire of Thy chast -'ning,
4. So shall Thy chil - dren with thank - ful de - vo - tion

Thy ways of bless - ed - ness, slight - ed Thy word;
Yet to e - ter - ni - ty stand - eth Thy word;
Earth shall to free - dom and truth be re - stored;
Praise Him who saved them from per - il and sword,

Bid not Thy wrath in its ter - rors a - wak - en;
False - hood and wrong shall not tar - ry be - side Thee:
Through the thick dark - ness Thy king - dom is hast -'ning:
Sing - ing in cho - rus from o - cean to o - cean,

Give to us peace in our time, O Lord!
Give to us peace in our time, O Lord!
Thou wilt give peace to Thy time, O Lord!
Peace to the na - tions and praise to the Lord. A - men.

91
God of Grace and God of Glory

CWM RHONDDA. 8. 7. 8. 7. 8. 7.

Harry Emerson Fosdick, b. 1878

Welsh hymn melody
John Hughes, 1873-1932

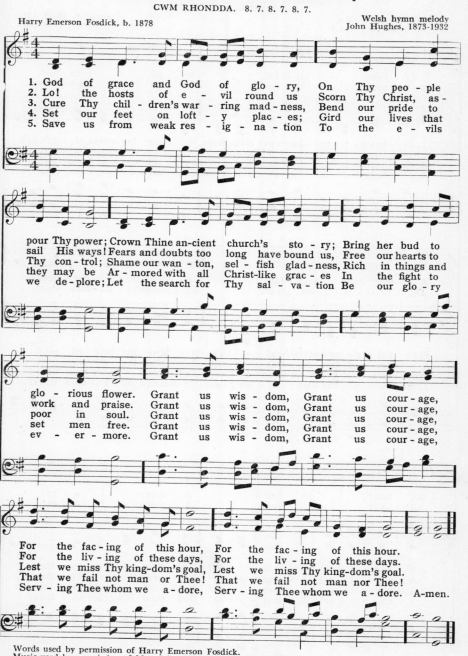

1. God of grace and God of glo - ry, On Thy peo - ple
2. Lo! the hosts of e - vil round us Scorn Thy Christ, as -
3. Cure Thy chil - dren's war - ring mad - ness, Bend our pride to
4. Set our feet on loft - y plac - es; Gird our lives that
5. Save us from weak res - ig - na - tion To the e - vils

pour Thy power; Crown Thine an-cient church's sto - ry; Bring her bud to
sail His ways! Fears and doubts too long have bound us, Free our hearts to
Thy con - trol; Shame our wan - ton, sel - fish glad - ness, Rich in things and
they may be Ar - mored with all Christ-like grac - es In the fight to
we de - plore; Let the search for Thy sal - va - tion Be our glo - ry

glo - rious flower. Grant us wis - dom, Grant us cour - age,
work and praise. Grant us wis - dom, Grant us cour - age,
poor in soul. Grant us wis - dom, Grant us cour - age,
set men free. Grant us wis - dom, Grant us cour - age,
ev - er - more. Grant us wis - dom, Grant us cour - age,

For the fac - ing of this hour, For the fac - ing of this hour.
For the liv - ing of these days, For the liv - ing of these days.
Lest we miss Thy king-dom's goal, Lest we miss Thy king-dom's goal.
That we fail not man or Thee! That we fail not man nor Thee!
Serv - ing Thee whom we a - dore, Serv - ing Thee whom we a - dore. A-men.

92 America, the Beautiful

MATERNA. C. M. D.

Katharine Lee Bates, 1904
Descant for stanzas 2 and 4

Samuel A. Ward, 1882
Descant by Peter W. Dykema

2. O beau - ti - ful for pil - grim feet,
4. O beau - ti - ful for pa - triot dream,

1. O beau - ti - ful for spa - cious skies, For am - ber waves of grain,
2. O beau - ti - ful for pil - grim feet Whose stern im - pas-sioned stress
3. O beau - ti - ful for he - roes proved In lib - er - at - ing strife,
4. O beau - ti - ful for pa - triot dream That sees be - yond the years

A thor - ough - fare a - cross the wil - der - ness.
Thy cit - ies gleam Un-dimmed by hu - man tears.

For pur - ple moun-tain maj - es - ties A - bove the fruit - ed plain.
A thor-ough-fare for free - dom beat A - cross the wil - der - ness.
Who more than self their Coun - try loved, And mer - cy more than life.
Thine al - a - bas - ter cit - ies gleam Un-dimmed by hu - man tears.

All hail! All hail! A - mer - i - ca!
All hail! All hail! A - mer - i - ca!

A - mer - i - ca! A - mer - i - ca! God shed His grace on thee,
A - mer - i - ca! A - mer - i - ca! God mend thine ev - 'ry flaw,
A - mer - i - ca! A - mer - i - ca! May God thy gold re - fine
A - mer - i - ca! A - mer - i - ca! God shed His grace on thee,

All hail! All hail! Thy lib - er - ty in law.
All hail! All hail! From sea to shin - ing sea!

And crown thy good with broth - er - hood From sea to shin - ing sea!
Con - firm thy soul in self - con - trol, Thy lib - er - ty in law.
Till all suc - cess be no - ble - ness And ev - 'ry gain di - vine.
And crown thy good with broth - er - hood From sea to shin - ing sea!

93   My Country, 'Tis of Thee

AMERICA. 6. 6. 4. 6. 6. 6. 4.

Samuel F. Smith, 1832   Henry Carey, 1743

1. My coun - try, 'tis of thee, Sweet land of lib - er - ty,
2. My na - tive coun - try, thee, Land of the no - ble free,
3. Let mu - sic swell the breeze, And ring from all the trees
4. Our fa - thers' God, to Thee, Auth - or of lib - er - ty,

Of thee I sing; Land where my fa - thers died, Land of the
Thy name I love; I love thy rocks and rills, Thy woods and
Sweet free - dom's song: Let mor - tal tongues a - wake; Let all that
To Thee we sing: Long may our land be bright With free - dom's

pil - grim's pride, From ev - 'ry moun - tain side Let free - dom ring.
tem - pled hills; My heart with rap - ture thrills Like that a - bove.
breathe partake; Let rocks their si - lence break, The sound pro - long.
ho - ly light; Pro - tect us by Thy might, Great God, our King. A - men.

94 Judge Eternal, Throned in Splendor

SWANSEA. 8. 7. 8. 7. 8. 7.

Henry Scott Holland, 1847-1918

From a Basque Church Melody

1. Judge E - ter - nal, throned in splen - dor, Lord of lords and
King of kings, With Thy liv - ing fire of judg - ment
Purge this land of bit - ter things; Sol - ace all its
wide do - min - ion With the heal - ing of Thy wings.

2. Still the wea - ry folk are pin - ing For the hour that
brings re - lease; And the cit - y's crowd - ed clan - gor
Cries a - loud for sin to cease; And the home - steads
and the wood - lands Plead in si - lence for their peace.

3. Crown, O God, Thine own en - deav - or; Cleave our dark - ness
with Thy sword; Feed the faint and hun - gry peo - ples
With the rich - ness of Thy word; Cleanse the bod - y
of this na - tion Through the glo - ry of the Lord.

95 O, Hear Them Marching, Marching

GREENLAND. 7. 6. 7. 6. D.

Marion Franklin Ham, b. 1867

Arr. from Johann Michael Haydn, 1737-1806
In B. Jacob's *National Psalmody*, 1819

1. O, hear them march-ing, march - ing, The le - gions of good will,
2. Through all the blood-stained a - ges Their num - bers have in-creased,
3. The men of war op - pose them, And seek to bar the way,
4. A might - y cap - tain leads them, The val - iant Prince of Peace;

The men of peace who seek not To bomb and maim and kill;
The spir - it strug-gling up - ward To o - ver - come the beast;
The pow'rs of dark - ness striv - ing To thwart the com - ing day;
They shall pos - sess the fu - ture, And an - cient wrongs shall cease;

They march not to their con - quest With bat - tle flags un - furled;
The meek who shall in - her - it And rule the war - ring earth,
But led by un - seen forc - es, Their hosts are march - ing still
O men of good - will march - ing To blood - less vic - to - ry,

But with their gen - tle spir - it They shall sub-due the world.
With pa - tient faith are bring - ing The new re - gime to birth.
To build for fu - ture a - ges The king-dom of good will.
We join your hosts in build - ing The king-dom that shall be. A-men.

Words used by permission of the author.

96 When Morning Gilds the Skies

LAUDES DOMINI. 6. 6. 6. 6. 6. 6.

From the German
Tr. by Edward Caswall, 1853

Joseph Barnby, 1868

1. When morn - ing gilds the skies, My heart a - wak - ing cries:
2. Does sad - ness fill my mind, A sol - ace here I find:
3. In heaven's e - ter - nal bliss The love - liest strain is this,
4. Be this, while life is mine, My can - ti - cle di - vine,

May Je - sus Christ be praised! A - like at work or prayer
May Je - sus Christ be praised! Or fades my earth - ly bliss,
May Je - sus Christ be praised! The powers of dark - ness fear,
May Je - sus Christ be praised! Be this th' e - ter - nal song,

To Je - sus I re - pair: May Je - sus Christ be praised!
My com - fort still is this: May Je - sus Christ be praised!
When this sweet chant they hear: May Je - sus Christ be praised!
Through all the a - ges long: May Je - sus Christ be praised! A-men.

97 New Every Morning Is the Love

MELCOMBE. L. M.

John Keble, 1822

Samuel Webbe, 1792

1. New ev - ery morn-ing is the love Our wak-ening and up - ris - ing prove—
2. New mer - cies, each re - turn-ing day, Hov - er a - round us while we pray;
3. If on our dai - ly course our mind Be set to hal - low all we find,
4. The tri - vial round, the com-mon task, Will fur - nish all we ought to ask,—
5. On - ly, O Lord, in Thy dear love, Fit us for per - fect rest a - bove,

Through sleep and darkness safe-ly brought, Restored to life, and power, and thought.
New per-ils past, new sins forgiven, New thoughts of God, new hopes of heaven.
New treas-ures still, of count-less price, God will pro-vide for sac-ri-fice.
Room to de-ny our-selves, a road To bring us dai-ly near-er God.
And help us, this and ev-ery day, To live more near-ly as we pray. A-men.

98 Still, Still With Thee

CONSOLATION. 11. 10. 11. 10.

Harriet Beecher Stowe, 1855

Felix Mendelssohn-Bartholdy, 1809-1847

1. Still, still with Thee, when pur-ple morn-ing break-eth, When the bird
2. A-lone with Thee, a-mid the mys-tic shad-ows, The sol-emn
3. When sinks the soul, sub-dued by toil, to slum-ber, Its clos-ing
4. So shall it be at last, in that bright morn-ing When the soul

wak-eth, and the shad-ows flee; Fair-er than morn-ing, love-lier than the
hush of na-ture new-ly born; A-lone with Thee in breath-less ad-o-
eyes look up to Thee in prayer; Sweet the re-pose be-neath Thy wings o'er
wak-eth, and life's shad-ows flee; O in that hour, fair-er than day-light

day-light, Dawns the sweet con-scious-ness, I am with Thee.
ra-tion, In the calm dew and fresh-ness of the morn.
shad-ing, But sweet-er still to wake and find Thee there.
dawn-ing, Shall rise the glo-rious thought—I am with Thee. A-men.

99 Now the Day Is Over

MERRIAL. 6. 5. 6. 5.

Rev. Sabine Baring-Gould, 1865   Joseph Barnby, 1868

1. Now the day is o - ver, Night is draw - ing nigh,
2. Je - sus, give the wea - ry Calm and sweet re - pose;
3. Grant to lit - tle chil - dren Vi - sions bright of Thee;
4. Through the long night watch - es, May Thine an - gels spread
5. When the morn - ing wak - ens, Then may I a - rise

Shad - ows of the eve - ning Steal a - cross the sky.
With Thy ten-derest bless - ing May mine eye - lids close.
Guard the sail - ors toss - ing On the deep blue sea.
Their white wings a - bove me, Watch - ing round my bed.
Pure, and fresh, and sin - less In Thy ho - ly eyes. A - men.

Words used by permission of A. W. Ridley and Company.

100 All Praise to Thee, My God, This Night

Thomas Ken, 1637-1711   TALLIS' CANON. L. M.
Text of 1709   Thomas Tallis, c. 1520-1585

1. All praise to Thee, my God, this night, For all the bless-ings of the light;
2. For - give me, Lord, for Thy dear Son, The ill that I this day have done;
3. O may my soul on Thee re - pose, And with sweet sleep mine eye-lids close;
4. Praise God, from whom all bless-ings flow; Praise Him, all crea-tures here be - low;

Keep me, O keep me, King of kings, Be-neath Thine own al-might - y wings.
That with the world, my-self, and Thee, I, ere I sleep, at peace may be.
Sleep that may me more vig-orous make To serve my God when I a - wake.
Praise Him a - bove, ye heaven-ly host; Praise Fa-ther, Son, and Ho - ly Ghost. A-men.

May be sung as a canon in two parts—women and boys singing the soprano, men the tenor. The fifth note in the tenor begins the imitation of the soprano.

101 Day Is Dying in the West

CHAUTAUQUA. 7. 7. 7. 7. 4.

Mary A. Lathbury, 1877

William F. Sherwin, 1877

1. Day is dy-ing in the west; Heaven is touch-ing earth with rest; Wait and
2. Lord of life, be-neath the dome Of the un - i - verse, Thy home, Gath - er
3. While the deepening shadows fall, Heart of love, en - fold-ing all, Through the
4. When for ev - er from our sight Pass the stars, the day, the night, Lord of

wor-ship while the night Sets her eve-ning lamps a-light Through all the sky.
us who seek Thy face To the fold of Thy em-brace, For Thou art nigh.
glo - ry and the grace Of the stars that veil Thy face, Our hearts as - cend.
an - gels, on our eyes Let e - ter - nal morn-ing rise, And shad-ows end.

Refrain

Ho - ly, ho - ly, ho - ly, Lord God of hosts! Heaven and earth are

full of Thee; Heaven and earth are prais-ing Thee, O Lord Most High. A-men.

By permission of Chautauqua Instituion, Chautauqua, New York.

102 Now, on Land and Sea Descending

VESPER HYMN. 8. 7. 8. 7. 8. 6. 8. 7.

Samuel Longfellow, 1819-1892, alt.

Dimitri S. Bortniansky, 1752-1825

1. Now, on land and sea de-scend-ing, Brings the night its peace pro-found;
2. Soon as dies the sun-set glo-ry, Stars of heaven shine out a-bove,
3. Now, our wants and bur-dens leav-ing To His care who cares for all,
4. As the dark-ness deep-ens o'er us, Lo! e-ter-nal stars a-rise;

Let our ves-per hymn be blend-ing With the ho-ly calm a-round.
Tell-ing still the an-cient sto-ry— Their Cre-a-tor's change-less love.
Cease we fear-ing, cease we griev-ing: At His touch our bur-dens fall.
Hope and faith and love rise glo-rious, Shin-ing in the spir-it's skies.

Ju-bi-la-te! Ju-bi-la-te! Ju-bi-la-te! A-men.

Let our ves-per hymn be blend-ing With the ho-ly calm a-round.
Tell-ing still the an-cient sto-ry—Their Cre-a-tor's changeless love.
Cease we fear-ing, cease we griev-ing: At His touch our bur-dens fall.
Hope and faith and love rise glo-rious, Shin-ing in the spir-it's skies. A-men.

103 Not Alone for Mighty Empire

IN BABILONE. 8. 7. 8. 7. 8. 7. 8. 7.

William Pierson Merrill, 1911

Dutch Traditional Melody
Arranged

1. Not a - lone for might - y em - pire, Stretch-ing far o'er land and sea,
2. Not for bat - tle - ship and for-tress, Not for con - quests of the sword,
3. For the ar-mies of the faith-ful, Lives that passed and left no name;
4. God of jus-tice, save the peo - ple From the clash of race and creed,

Not a - lone for boun - teous har-vests, Lift we up our hearts to Thee.
But for con-quests of the spir - it Give we thanks to Thee, O Lord;
For the glo - ry that il - lu-mines Pa - triot souls of death-less fame;
From the strife of class and fac - tion, Make our na - tion free in - deed.

Stand - ing in the liv - ing pres-ent, Mem - o - ry and hope be - tween,
For the her - it - age of free-dom, For the home, the church, the school,
For the peo-ple's proph - et - lead - ers, Loy - al to Thy liv - ing Word,
Keep her faith in sim - ple man-hood Strong as when her life be - gan,

Lord, we would with deep thanks-giv-ing Praise Thee most for things un-seen.
For the o - pen door to man-hood In a land the peo - ple rule.
For all he - roes of the spir - it, Give we thanks to Thee, O Lord.
Till it finds its full fru - i - tion In the broth-er - hood of man! A-men.

Tune used by permission of Professor Julius Rontgen.

104   We Plow the Fields, and Scatter

WIR PFLÜGEN. 7. 6. 7. 6. D. with Refrain.

Matthias Claudius, 1782
Tr. Jane M. Campbell, 1861

Johann A. P. Schulz, 1800

1. We plow the fields, and scat-ter The good seed on the land,
2. He on-ly is the Mak-er Of all things near and far;
3. We thank Thee, then, O Fa-ther, For all things bright and good,

But it is fed and wa-tered By God's al-might-y hand;
He paints the way-side flow-er, He lights the eve-ning star;
The seed-time and the har-vest, Our life, our health, our food;

He sends the snow in win-ter, The warmth to swell the grain,
The winds and waves o-bey Him, By Him the birds are fed;
No gifts have we to of-fer, For all Thy love im-parts,

The breez-es and the sun-shine, And soft re-fresh-ing rain.
Much more to us, His chil-dren, He gives our dai-ly bread.
But that which Thou de-sir-est, Our hum-ble, thank-ful hearts.

Refrain

All good gifts a-round us Are sent from heaven a-bove;

Then thank the Lord, O thank the Lord For all His love. A-men.

105 Praise God from Whom All Blessings Flow

OLD 100th. L. M.

Thomas Ken, 1709

Louis Bourgeois, 1551

Praise God, from whom all bless-ings flow; Praise Him, all crea-tures here be-low;

Praise Him a-bove, ye heaven-ly host; Praise Fa-ther, Son, and Ho-ly Ghost. A-men.

106 Fourfold Amen

John Stainer

p *cres.* *mf* *dim.*

A - men, A - men, A - - - men, A - men.

SPIRITUALS
Couldn't Hear Nobody Pray

(H. M.)

O I could-n't hear no-bod-y pray (O Lord) I could-n't hear no-bod-y pray, Oh way down yon-der by my-self, I could-n't hear no-bod-y pray.

1. In the val-ley, Could-n't hear no-bod-y pray. On my knees, Could-n't hear no-bod-y pray. With my bur-den, Could-n't hear no-bod-y pray. And my Sav-ior Could-n't hear no-bod-y pray. O Lord, I

2. Chilly waters, In the Jordan,
Crossing over into Canaan.

3. Hallelujah! Troubles over!
In the kingdom With my Jesus.

108   Go Down, Moses

(H. M.)

1. When Is - rael was in E - gypt's land, Let my peo - ple go!

Op - pressed so hard they could not stand, Let my peo - ple go!

Go down, Mo - ses, 'Way down in E - gypt's land.

Tell old Pha - roah, Let my peo - ple go!

2 "Thus saith the Lord," bold Moses said,
  If not, I'll smite your first-born dead,

3 No more shall they in bondage toil,
  Let them come out with Egypt's spoil.

4 Your foes shall not before you stand,
  And you'll possess fair Canaan's land.

5 O let us all from bondage flee,
  And let us all in Christ be free.

109 Everytime I Feel the Spirit

(H. M.)

Ev - ery time I feel the Spir - it Mov - ing in my heart I will

Fine

pray pray; 1. Jor-dan's Riv - er, chill - y cold, Chills the bod - y not the

D. C.

soul Upon the moun-tain my Lord spoke. Out His mouth came fire and smoke.

2 In the valley, on my knees,
Ask my Lord have mercy, please.
All around me looks so fine,
Ask my Lord if all is mine.

3 I have sorrows, I have woe,
I have heartache here below;
But God leads me, I'll not fear,
I am sheltered by his care.

110 He's Got the Whole World in His Hand

1. He's got the whole world in His hand, He's got the

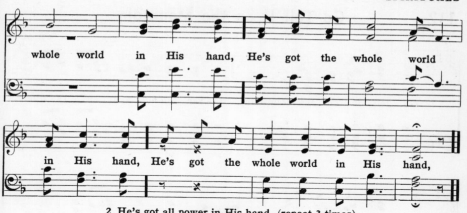

whole world in His hand, He's got the whole world

in His hand, He's got the whole world in His hand,

2 He's got all power in His hand, (repeat 3 times)
He's got the whole world in His hand.
3 He's got my mother in His hand,
He's got the whole world in His hand.
4 He's got my father in His hand,
He's got the whole world in His hand.
5 He's got the whole church in His hand,
He's got the whole world in His hand.

111　　　**Jacob's Ladder**

1. We are climb - ing Ja - cob's lad - der, We are

climb - ing Ja - cob's lad - der, We are climb - ing

Ja - cob's lad - der Sol - diers of the Cross.

2 Ev'ry round goes higher, higher, . . .
3 Sinner, do you love your Jesus? . . .
4 If you love Him, why not serve Him? . . .
5 Rise—, shine—, give God glory.
6 We are climbing higher, higher.

112 Go Tell It on the Mountain

(Christmas)

(H. M.)

Go tell it on the moun-tain, O - ver the hills and ev' - ry - where.

Go tell it on the moun - tain that Je - sus Christ is born.

1. When I was a sin - ner, I prayed both night and day. I

Hum——

asked the Lord to help me, And he showed me the way.

Hum——

D. C. al Fine

2 When I was a seeker, I sought both night and day
  I asked my Lord to help me, and He taught me to pray.

3 He made me a watchman upon the city wall;
  And if I am a Christian, I am the least of all.

113 Lord, I Want to Be a Christian

1. Lord, I want to be a Chris-tian In - a my heart, in - a my
2. Lord, I want to be more lov - ing In - a my heart, in - a my
3. Lord, I want to be more ho - ly In - a my heart, in - a my
4. Lord, I want to be like Je - sus In - a my heart, in - a my

heart, Lord, I want to be a Chris-tian In - a my heart.—
heart, Lord, I want to be more lov - ing In - a my heart.—
heart, Lord, I want to be more ho - ly In - a my heart.—
heart, Lord, I want to be like Je - sus In - a my heart.—

Refrain

In - a my heart,———— In - a my heart,————

In - a my heart, In - a my heart,

Lord, I want to be a Chris - tian In - a my heart.—
Lord, I want to be more lov - ing In - a my heart.—
Lord, I want to be more ho - ly In - a my heart.—
Lord, I want to be like Je - sus In - a my heart.—

114   I Know the Lord

(H. M.)

O I know the Lord, I know the Lord, I know the Lord laid His

hands on me hands on me. 1. O was-n't that a might-y day?
2. Did e'er you see the light be - fore,

I know the Lord laid His hands on me When Je - sus washed your
King Je - sus preach - ing

D. C.

sins a - way. I know the Lord laid His hands on me.
to the poor.

115   I Want Jesus to Walk with Me

(H. M.)

1. I want Je - sus to walk with me; (walk with me) I want

Je - sus to walk with me; (walk with me) All a - long my pil - grim

jour - ney, Lord, I want Je - sus to walk with me.

2. In my trials, Lord walk with me;
In my trials, Lord walk with me;
When my heart is almost breaking,
Lord, I want Jesus to walk with me.

3. In my troubles, Lord walk with me;
In my troubles, Lord walk with me;
When my head is bowed in sorrow,
Lord, I want Jesus to walk with me.

116   My Lord, What a Morning

Refrain

My Lord, what a morn-ing, My Lord, what a morn-ing, My Lord, what a

morn-ing, When the stars be-gin to fall.

Fine   *Solo*

1. You'll hear the trumpet sound, To wake the
2. You'll hear the sin-ner mourn,
3. You'll hear the Christian shout,

D. C.

nations underground, Looking to my God's right hand, When the stars be-gin to fall.

117 Let Us Break Bread Together

(H. M.)

1. Let us break bread to-geth-er on our knees, (yes on our knees.) Let us break bread to-geth-er on our knees, (yes on our knees.) When I fall on my knees with my face to the ris-ing sun, O Lord have mer-cy on me, (on me).

2. Let us drink wine together on our knees,

3. Let us praise God together on our knees,

118   Nobody Knows the Trouble I've Seen

(H. M.)

Oh, no-bod-y knows the trou-ble I've seen, No-bod-y knows but

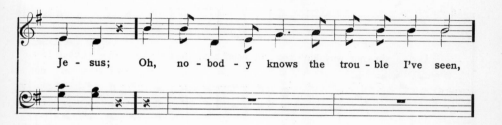

Je - sus; Oh, no-bod-y knows the trou-ble I've seen,

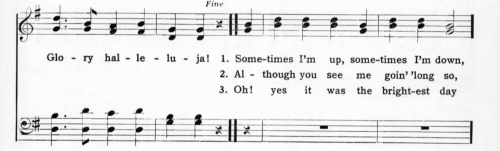

Fine

Glo - ry hal - le - lu - ja!
1. Some-times I'm up, some-times I'm down,
2. Al - though you see me goin' 'long so,
3. Oh! yes it was the bright-est day

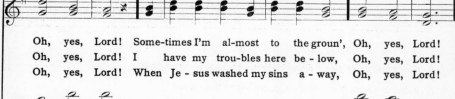

D. C.

Oh, yes, Lord! Some-times I'm al-most to the groun', Oh, yes, Lord!
Oh, yes, Lord! I have my trou-bles here be - low, Oh, yes, Lord!
Oh, yes, Lord! When Je - sus washed my sins a - way, Oh, yes, Lord!

119 Somebody's Knocking At Your Door

Some-bod-y's knock-ing at your door, Some-bod-y's knock-ing at your door

O sin-ner why don't you an-swer? Some-bod-y's knock-ing at your door.

1. Knocks like Je-sus, Some-bod-y's knock-ing at your door

Knocks like Je-sus, Some-bod-y's knock-ing at your door.

2. Can't you hear Him? Somebody's knocking at your door

3. Answer Jesus, Somebody's knocking at your door

4. Jesus calls you, Somebody's knocking at your door

5. Can't you trust Him? Somebody's knocking at your door

120   # Standin' in the Need of Prayer

(H. M.)

It's me————,

it's me, it's me O Lord, Stand-in' in the need of prayer.

It's me————,

Fine

it's me, it's me O Lord, stand-in' in the need of prayer.

1. Not my broth-er but it's me O Lord, stand-in' in the need of prayer

D. C.

Not my broth-er but it's me O Lord, stand-in' in the need of prayer.

2. sister

3. mother

4. father

5. preacher

121 Study War No More

(H. M.)

1. Gwine to lay down my bur - den, Down by the riv - er side, Down by the
riv - er side, Down by the riv - er side, Gwine to lay down my bur - den,
Down by the riv - er side to stud - y war no more. I ain't gwine

Refrain

stud - y war no more, ain't gwine stud - y war no more, ain't gwine stud - y
war no more I ain't gwine stud - y war no more,
stud - y war no more

Ain't gwine stud-y war no more, Ain't gwine stud-y war no more.

2. Gwine to lay down my sword and shield,
3. Gwine to try on my long white robe,
4. Gwine to try on my starry crown,

122 Steal Away

(H. M.)

Steal a - way, steal a - way, steal a - way to Je - sus.

Steal a - way, Steal a - way home, I ain't got long to stay here.

1. My Lord, He calls me, He calls me by the thun - der. The

Trum-pet sounds with - in - a my soul. I ain't got long to stay here.

2. Green trees abending, Poor sinner stand a trembling,
3. My Lord, He calls me, He calls me by the lightning.

123 Swing Low, Sweet Chariot

Swing low sweet char-i-ot, Com-ing for to car-ry me home.

Swing low sweet char-i-ot Com-ing for to car-ry me home.

Fine

1. I looked o-ver Jor-dan and what did I see
2. If you get there be-fore I do,
3. I'm some-times up I'm some-times down,

Com-ing for to car-ry me home. A band of an-gels
Com-ing for to car-ry me home. Tell all my friends I'm
Com-ing for to car-ry me home. But still my soul feels

D. C.

com-ing aft-er me— Com-ing for to car-ry me home.
com-ing too, Com-ing for to car-ry me home.
heav-en-ly bound, Com-ing for to car-ry me home.

124 Were You There

(H. M.)

1. Were you there when they cru - ci - fied my Lord? (Were you there)

Were you there when they cru - ci - fied my Lord? (Were you there)

Oh! .... Some-times it caus - es me to trem-ble, trem-ble,

trem-ble, Were you there when they cru - ci - fied my Lord? (Were you there)

2. Were you there when they nailed Him to the tree?

3. Were you there when they pierced Him in the side?

4. Were you there when the sun refused to shine?

5. Were you there when they laid Him in the tomb?

125
Balm in Gilead

(H. M.)

There is a Balm in Gil - e - ad To make the wound-ed whole

There is a balm in Gil - e - ad To heal the sin - sick soul. *Fine*

1. Some times I feel dis - cour-aged, And think my works in vain, But

Hum

then the Ho - ly Spir - it, Re - vives my soul a - gain. *D. C.*

2. Don't ever feel discouraged,
   For Jesus is your Friend,
   And if you lack for knowledge,
   He'll not refuse to lend.

3. If you cannot preach like Peter,
   If you cannot pray like Paul,
   You can tell the love of Jesus
   And say, "He died for all."

126 Burden Down

(H. M.)

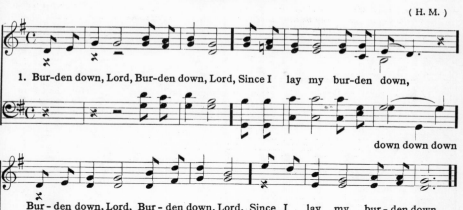

1. Bur-den down, Lord, Bur-den down, Lord, Since I lay my bur-den down,

down down down

Bur - den down, Lord, Bur - den down, Lord, Since I lay my bur - den down.

2. Wonder will my sister know me, Since I lay my burden down, . . .
3. Wonder will my brother know me, Since I lay my burden down, . . .
4. Burden down, Lord, Burden down, Lord, Since I lay my burden down, . . .

127 Lord, Make Me More Holy

Negro Spiritual

1. Lord, make me more ho - ly, Lord, make me more ho - ly, Lord, make me more ho - ly,

un - til we meet a - gain. Ho - ly, ho - ly, ho - ly, un - til we meet a - gain.

2. Faithful... 3. Humble... 4. Righteous...

128 Lonesome Valley

A deeply sincere and beautiful spiritual arisen from the fervor of white people's "camp-meetings."
The first and third verses may be sung as solos preferably by a man, while the chorus "walks" its part.
The second verse may be sung in unison.
In moderate walking time.

White Spiritual from the
Southern Highlands, U. S. A.

mf Solo

1. Je - sus walk'd this lone-some val - ley, He had to
2. We must walk this lone-some val - ley, We have to
3. You must go and stand your trial, You have to

1. Je - sus walk'd this lone - some val - ley,
3. You must go and stand your tri - al,

walk it by Him-self, Oh, no - bod - y else could
walk it by our-selves, Oh, no - bod - y else can
stand it by your-self, Oh, no - bod - y else can

gradually a little louder, but still soft

Had to walk it by Him - self, Oh, no one else
Have to stand it by your - self, Oh, no one else

walk it for Him, He had to walk it by Him-self.
walk it for us, We have to walk it by our-selves.
stand it for you. You have to stand it by your-self.

softer

could walk it for Him, Had to walk it by Him-self.
can stand it for you. Have to stand it for your-self.

From the collection, and adapted from the arrangement made by Gladys Jameson of Berea College, Kentucky.

This arrangement from *Singing America*. Used by permission of C. C. Birchard & Co.

129 Wondrous Love

Southern Folk Hymn
Arr. by Irving Wolfe

Unison

1. What won-drous love is this, O my soul, O my soul! What won-drous love is this, O my soul! What won-drous love is this that caused the Lord of bliss To bear the dread-ful curse for my soul, for my soul, To bear the dread-ful curse for my soul.

2. When I was sink-ing down, sink-ing down, sink-ing down, When I was sink-ing down, sink-ing down, When I was sink-ing down be-neath God's right-eous frown, Christ laid a-side His crown for my soul, for my soul, Christ laid a-side His crown for my soul.

3. To God and to the Lamb I will sing, I will sing, To God and to the Lamb I will sing, To God and to the Lamb who is the great I am, While mil-lions join the theme, I will sing, I will sing, While mil-lions join the theme, I will sing.

4. And when from death I'm free, I'll sing on, I'll sing on, And when from death I'm free, I'll sing on, And when from death I'm free, I'll sing and joy-ful be, And thru e-ter-ni-ty I'll sing on, I'll sing on, And thru e-ter-ni-ty I'll sing on.

Used by permission.

130 Wayfaring Stranger

(H. M.)

1. I am a poor way-far-ing stran-ger a-trav-'ling through this world of woe, Yet there's no sick-ness toil or dan-ger, In that bright land to which I go. I'm go-ing there to see my fa-ther, I'm go-ing there no more to roam, I'm just a-go-ing o-ver Jor-dan, I'm just a-go-ing o-ver home.

2. I'll soon be freed of ev'ry trial,
My body asleep in the old church yard.
I'll drop the cross of self-denial,
And enter on my great reward.
I'm going there to see my Savior,
To sing His praise forever more.
I'm just a going over Jordan,
I'm just a going over home.

131   All the Way My Saviour Leads Me

Fanny J. Crosby, 1820-1915   Robert Lowry, 1826-1899

1. All the way my Sav-iour leads me; What have I to ask be-side?
2. All the way my Sav-iour leads me, Cheers each wind-ing path I tread,
3. All the way my Sav-iour leads me; Oh, the full-ness of His love!

Can I doubt His ten-der mer-cy, Who through life has been my Guide?
Gives me grace for ev-ery tri-al, Feeds me with the liv-ing bread.
Per-fect rest to me is prom-ised In my Fa-ther's house a-bove.

Heaven-ly peace, di-vin-est com-fort, Here my faith in Him to dwell!
Though my wea-ry steps may fal-ter, And my soul a-thirst may be,
When my spir-it, clothed im-mor-tal, Wings its flight to realms of day,

For I know, what-e'er be-fall me, Je-sus do-eth all things well; well.
Gush-ing from the Rock be-fore me, Lo! a spring of joy I see; see.
This my song through end-less a-ges; Je-sus led me all the way; way.

132   Blessed Assurance, Jesus Is Mine!

Fanny J. Crosby, 1873

Mrs. Joseph F. Knapp, 1873

1. Bless-ed as-sur-ance, Je-sus is mine! O what a fore-taste of glo-ry di-
2. Per-fect sub-mis-sion, per-fect de-light, Vi-sions of rap-ture now burst on my
3. Per-fect sub-mis-sion, all is at rest, I in my Sav-iour am hap-py and

vine! Heir of sal-va-tion, pur-chase of God, Born of His
sight; An-gels de-scend-ing, bring from a-bove, Ech-oes of
blest, Watch-ing and wait-ing, look-ing a-bove, Filled with His

Refrain

Spir-it, washed in His blood. This is my sto-ry, this is my
mer-cy, whis-pers of love.
good-ness, lost in His love.

song, Prais-ing my Sav-iour all the day long; This is my

sto-ry, this is my song, Prais-ing my Sav-iour all the day long.

133 God Be With You Till We Meet Again

Jeremiah E. Rankin, 1882

William G. Tomer, 1882

1. God be with you till we meet a-gain, By His coun-sels guide, up-
2. God be with you till we meet a-gain, 'Neath His wings se-cure-ly
3. God be with you till we meet a-gain, When life's per-ils thick con-
4. God be with you till we meet a-gain, Keep love's ban-ner float-ing

hold you, With His sheep se-cure-ly fold you, God be with you
hide you, Dai-ly man-na still pro-vide you, God be with you
found you, Put His arms un-fail-ing round you, God be with you
o'er you, Smite death's threat'ning wave be-fore you, God be with you

Refrain

till we meet a-gain. Till we meet till we meet,
Till we meet, till we meet,

Till we meet at Je-sus' feet; Till we meet,
Till we meet, till we meet,

Till we meet, God be with you till we meet a-gain.
till we meet;

134   He Leadeth Me, O Blessed Thought

Joseph H. Gilmore, 1859   William B. Bradbury, 1864

1. He lead-eth me: O bless-ed tho't! O words with heavenly comfort fraught!
2. Some-times 'mid scenes of deep-est gloom, Sometimes where E - den's bow-ers bloom,
3. Lord, I would clasp Thy hand in mine, Nor ev - er mur - mur nor re-pine;
4. And when my task on earth is done, When, by thy grace, the vic-t'ry's won,

What - e'er I do, wher - e'er I be, Still 'tis God's hand that lead-eth me.
By wa - ters calm, o'er trou-bled sea,—Still 'tis His hand that lead-eth me.
Con - tent, what-ev - er lot I see, Since 'tis my God that lead-eth me.
E'en death's cold wave I will not flee, Since God thro' Jor - dan lead-eth me.

Refrain

He lead-eth me, He lead - eth me, By His own hand He lead-eth me:

His faith - ful fol-lower I would be, For by His hand He lead - eth me.

135 I Am Thine, O Lord

Fanny J. Crosby, 1820-1915

William H. Doane, 1832-1916

1. I am Thine, O Lord, I have heard Thy voice, And it told Thy love to
2. Con - se - crate me now to Thy serv-ice, Lord, By the pow'r of grace di -
3. O the pure de - light of a sin - gle hour That be - fore Thy throne I
4. There are depths of love that I can-not know Till I cross the nar - row

me; But I long to rise in the arms of faith, And be
vine; Let my soul look up with a stead - fast hope, And my
spend, When I kneel in prayer, and with Thee, my God, I com -
sea; There are heights of joy that I may not reach Till I

Refrain

clos - er drawn to Thee. Draw me near - er, near-er, bless-ed Lord,
will be lost in Thine.
mune as friend with friend!
rest in peace with Thee. near - er, near - er,

To the cross where Thou hast died; Draw me near - er, near - er,

near - er, bless - ed Lord, To Thy pre - cious, bleed - ing side.

136 I Love to Tell the Story

Katherine Hankey, 1870

William G. Fischer, 1869

1. I love to tell the sto - ry Of un - seen things a - bove, Of
2. I love to tell the sto - ry; More won - der - ful it seems Than
3. I love to tell the sto - ry; 'Tis pleas - ant to re - peat What
4. I love to tell the sto - ry; For those who know it best Seem

Je - sus and His glo - ry, Of Je - sus and His love. I love to tell the
all the gold - en fan - cies Of all our gold-en dreams. I love to tell the
seems, each time I tell it, More won-der-ful-ly sweet. I love to tell the
hun - ger - ing and thirst-ing To hear it, like the rest. And when, in scenes of

sto - ry, Be - cause I know it's true; It sat - is - fies my long-ings
sto - ry, It did so much for me; And that is just the rea - son
sto - ry, For some have nev - er heard The mes-sage of sal - va - tion
glo - ry, I sing the new, new song, 'Twill be the old, old sto - ry

Refrain

As noth - ing else would do.
I tell it now to thee. I love to tell the sto - ry, 'Twill be my theme in
From God's own ho - ly word.
That I have loved so long.

glo - ry,   To   tell   the   old, old   sto - ry   Of   Je - sus   and   His   love.

137   My Jesus, I Love Thee

Anonymous   Adoniram J. Gordon, 1878

1. My   Je - sus, I   love Thee, I know Thou art mine; For Thee all the   fol - lies
2. I   love Thee, be - cause Thou hast first lov-ed me,   And purchased my par - don
3. I will love Thee in   life,   I   will love Thee in death; And praise Thee as long   as
4. In   man-sions of   glo - ry and end-less de-light, I'll   ev - er   a - dore Thee

of   sin   I   re - sign; My   gra-cious Re - deem-er,   my   Sav - iour art   Thou;
on   Cal - va - ry's tree; I   love Thee for   wear-ing   the   thorns on Thy   brow;
Thou lend-est me breath; And   say, when the   death-dew lies   cold   on   my   brow,
in   heav - en   so bright; I'll   sing with the   glit - ter - ing   crown on   my   brow,

If   ev - er   I   loved Thee, my   Je - sus, 'tis   now.

138 I Need Thee Every Hour

Annie S. Hawks, 1872   Robert Lowry, 1872

1. I need Thee ev - 'ry hour, Most gra - cious Lord;
2. I need Thee ev - 'ry hour, Stay Thou near by;
3. I need Thee ev - 'ry hour, In joy or pain;
4. I need Thee ev - 'ry hour, Teach me Thy will;
5. I need Thee ev - 'ry hour, Most ho - ly One;

No ten - der voice like Thine Can peace af - ford.
Temp - ta - tions lose their pow'r When Thou art nigh.
Come quick - ly and a - bide, Or life is vain.
And Thy rich prom - is - es In me ful - fil.
O make me Thine in - deed, Thou bless - èd Son.

Refrain

I need Thee, O I need Thee, Ev - 'ry hour I need Thee;

O bless me now, my Sav - iour, I come to Thee.

139 I've Found a Friend

James G. Small, 1817-1888

George C. Stebbins, 1846

1. I've found a Friend, O such a Friend! He loved me ere I knew Him;
2. I've found a Friend, O such a Friend! He bled, He died to save me;
3. I've found a Friend, O such a Friend! So kind, and true, and ten-der,

He drew me with the cords of love, And thus He bound me to Him.
And not a-lone the gift of life, But His own self He gave me.
So wise a Coun-sel-or and Guide, So might-y a De-fend-er!

And 'round my heart still close-ly twine Those ties which naught can sev-er,
Naught that I have my own I call, I hold it for the Giv-er;
From Him who loves me now so well, What power my soul can sev-er?

For I am His, and He is mine, For ev-er and for ev-er.
My heart, my strength, my life, my all Are His, and His for ev-er.
Shall life or death, or earth or hell? No! I am His for ev-er.

140   Jesus, Keep Me Near the Cross

Fanny J. Crosby, 1820-1915   William H. Doane, 1832-1916

1. Je - sus, keep me near the cross; There a pre-cious foun-tain, Free to all, a
2. Near the cross, a trem-bling soul, Love and mer-cy found me; There the bright and
3. Near the cross! O Lamb of God, Bring its scenes be-fore me; Help me walk from

Refrain

heal - ing stream, Flows from Cal-v'ry's moun-tain.
Morn-ing Star Sheds its beams a - round me. In the cross, in the cross,
day to day, With its shad - ow o'er me.

Be my glo - ry ev - er, Till my rap-tured soul shall find Rest be-yond the riv - er.

141   He Cares for Me

Anonymous   James R. Murray

1. How strong and sweet my Fa-ther's care That round a - bout me, like the
2. O keep me ev - er in Thy love, Dear Fa - ther, watch-ing from a -

air, Is with me al-ways, ev-'ry-where! He cares for me.
bove, And as through life my steps shall move, O care for me.

142 More Love to Thee, O Christ

Mrs Elizabeth P. Prentiss, 1856   William H. Doane, 1832-1916

1. More love to Thee, O Christ, More love to Thee! Hear Thou the
2. Once earth-ly joy I craved, Sought peace and rest; Now Thee a-
3. Let sor-row do its work, Send grief and pain; Sweet are Thy
4. Then shall my lat-est breath Whis-per Thy praise; This be the

pray'r I make, On bend-ed knee; This is my ear-nest plea,
lone I seek, Give what is best; This all my pray'r shall be,
mes-sen-gers, Sweet their re-frain, When they can sing with me.
part-ing cry My heart shall raise, This still its pray'r shall be.

More love, O Christ, to Thee, More love to Thee, More love to Thee.

143 Savior, Make My Heart a Temple

Thomas Tiplady, 1944   Traditional

1. Sav - ior, make my heart a tem - ple For Thy wor-ship day and night;
2. Take my bod - y, mind and spir - it— Ev - ery la - tent power in me—
3. Yet, Lord, in the heat of bat - tle, Still a tem - ple be my heart

May its al - tar fires keep burn-ing With a clear and stead - y light!
In Thy fires and on Thine an - vil Fash - ion Lord, a sword for Thee!
Where the al - tar fires keep burn-ing, And Thy peace shall ne'er de - part;

Sanc - ti - fy me! Sanc - ti - fy me!

May its al - tar fires keep burn - ing, Make my heart Thy tem - ple, Lord.
In Thy fires and on Thine an - vil Fash - ion, Lord, a sword for Thee.
Where the al - tar fires keep burn - ing Make my heart Thy tem - ple Lord.

144 Great Is Thy Faithfulness

Thomas O. Chisholm   William M. Runyan

1. "Great is Thy faith-ful-ness," O God my Fa-ther, There is no shad-ow of
2. Sum-mer and win-ter, and spring-time and har-vest, Sun, moon and stars in their
3. Par-don for sin and a peace that en-dur-eth, Thy own dear pres-ence to

turn-ing with Thee; Thou chang-est not, Thy com-pas-sions, they fail not;
cours-es a-bove, Join with all na-ture in man-i-fold wit-ness
cheer and to guide; Strength for to-day and bright hope for to-mor-row,

Refrain

As Thou hast been Thou for-ev-er wilt be.
To Thy great faith-ful-ness, mer-cy and love. "Great is Thy faith-ful-ness!
Bless-ings all mine, with ten thou-sand be-side!

Great is Thy faith-ful-ness!" Morning by morning new mer-cies I see; All I have

rall.

need-ed Thy hand hath pro-vid-ed—"Great is Thy faith-ful-ness," Lord, un-to me!

145 Sing Them Over Again to Me

Philip P. Bliss

Philip P. Bliss, 1838-1876

1. Sing them o-ver a-gain to me, Won-der-ful words of
2. Christ, the bless-ed One, gives to all Won-der-ful words of
3. Sweet-ly ech-o the gos-pel call, Won-der-ful words of

life, Let me more of their beau-ty see, Won-der-ful words of
life, Sin-ner, list to the lov-ing call, Won-der-ful words of
life, Of-fer par-don and peace to all, Won-der-ful words of

life. Words of life and beau-ty, Teach me faith and du-ty;
life. All so free-ly giv-en Woo-ing us to heav-en,
life. Je-sus, on-ly Sav-iour Sanc-ti-fy for-ev-er,

Refrain

Beau-ti-ful words, won-der-ful words, Won-der-ful words of life,

Beau-ti-ful words, won-der-ful words, Won-der-ful words of life.

146 Sweet Hour of Prayer

William W. Walford, 1849

William B. Bradbury, 1859

1. Sweet hour of prayer! sweet hour of prayer! That calls me from a world of care,
2. Sweet hour of prayer! sweet hour of prayer! The joys I feel, the bliss I share,
3. Sweet hour of prayer! sweet hour of prayer! Thy wings shall my pe - ti - tion bear

And bids me at my Fa-ther's throne Make all my wants and wish-es known;
Of those whose anx-ious spir - its burn With strong de-sires for thy re-turn!
To Him whose truth and faith-ful-ness En - gage the wait-ing soul to bless;

In sea-sons of dis-tress and grief, My soul has oft - en found re - lief;
With such I has-ten to the place Where God my Sav - iour shows His face,
And since He bids me seek His face, Be - lieve His Word and trust His grace,

And oft es-caped the tempt-er's snare, By thy re-turn, sweet hour of prayer!
And glad - ly take my sta-tion there, And wait for thee, sweet hour of prayer!
I'll cast on Him my ev - ery care, And wait for thee, sweet hour of prayer!

147   Tell Me the Old, Old Story

Katherine Hankey, 1834-1911   William H. Doane, 1832-1916

1. Tell me the old, old sto-ry Of un-seen things a-bove, Of Je-sus and His glo-ry, Of Je-sus and His love. Tell me the sto-ry sim-ply, As to a lit-tle child; For I am weak and wea-ry, And help-less and de-filed.

2. Tell me the sto-ry slow-ly, That I may take it in— The won-der-ful re-demp-tion, God's rem-e-dy for sin. Tell me the sto-ry oft-en, For I for-get so soon; The ear-ly dew of morn-ing Has passed a-way at noon.

3. Tell me the sto-ry soft-ly, With ear-nest tones, and grave; Re-mem-ber, I'm the sin-ner Whom Je-sus came to save. Tell me that sto-ry al-ways, If you would real-ly be, In an-y time of trou-ble, A com-fort-er to me.

Refrain

Tell me the old, old sto-ry, Tell me the

old, old sto - ry. Tell me the old, old sto - ry Of Je - sus and His love.

148 Tell Me the Stories of Jesus

W. H. Parker, 1904

F. A. Challinor, 1904

1. Tell me the sto - ries of Je - sus I love to hear;
2. First let me hear how the chil - dren Stood round His knee;
3. In - to the cit - y I'd fol - low The chil - dren's band,
4. Tell me, in ac - cents of won - der, How rolled the sea,

Things I would ask Him to tell me If He were here; Scenes by the way-side,
And I shall fan-cy His bless-ing Rest-ing on me: Words full of kind-ness,
Wav - ing a branch of the palm-tree High in my hand; One of His her-alds,
Toss-ing the boat in a tem-pest On Gal - i - lee! And how the Mas-ter,

Tales of the sea, Sto - ries of Je - sus, Tell them to me.
Deeds full of grace, All in the love - light Of Je - sus' face.
Yes, I would sing Loud - est ho - san - nas! Je - sus is King!
Read - y and kind, Chid - ed the bil - lows, And hushed the wind.

149 Take the Name of Jesus with You

Lydia Baxter, 1809-1874

William H. Doane, 1832-1916

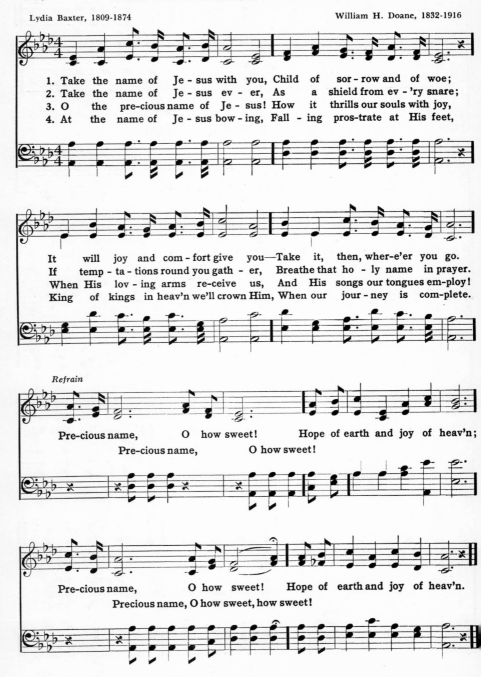

1. Take the name of Je - sus with you, Child of sor - row and of woe;
2. Take the name of Je - sus ev - er, As a shield from ev - 'ry snare;
3. O the pre-cious name of Je - sus! How it thrills our souls with joy,
4. At the name of Je - sus bow - ing, Fall - ing pros-trate at His feet,

It will joy and com - fort give you—Take it, then, wher-e'er you go.
If temp - ta - tions round you gath - er, Breathe that ho - ly name in prayer.
When His lov - ing arms re-ceive us, And His songs our tongues em-ploy!
King of kings in heav'n we'll crown Him, When our jour - ney is com-plete.

Refrain

Pre-cious name, O how sweet! Hope of earth and joy of heav'n;
Pre-cious name, O how sweet!

Pre-cious name, O how sweet! Hope of earth and joy of heav'n.
Precious name, O how sweet, how sweet!

150 True-Hearted, Whole-Hearted

Frances R. Havergal, 1874

George C. Stebbins, 1890

1. True-heart-ed, whole-heart-ed, faith-ful and loy - al, King of our lives, by Thy grace we will be; Un - der the stand-ard ex - alt - ed and roy - al, Strong in Thy strength we will bat-tle for Thee.
2. True-heart-ed, whole-heart-ed, full-est al - le-giance Yield-ing hence-forth to our glo - ri-ous King; Val - iant en-deav - or and lov - ing o-be-dience, Free - ly and joy - ous - ly now would we bring.
3. True-heart-ed, whole-heart-ed, Sav-iour all glo-rious! Take Thy great pow-er and reign there a - lone, O - ver our wills and af - fec - tions vic - to-rious, Free - ly sur-ren - dered and whol-ly Thine own.

Refrain

Peal out the watch-word! si - lence it nev-er! Song of our spir - its, re - joic - ing and free; Peal out the watch-word! loy - al for-ev - er, King of our lives, by Thy grace we will be.

151 Gott ist die Liebe

August Rische, 1819-1906
Tr. Anon.

Thüringer Weise, 1840

1. Gott ist die Lie-be, Lässt mich er-lö-sen; Gott ist die
For God so loved us, He sent the Sav-iour; For God so
2. Ich lag in Ban-den Der schnö-den Sün-de; Ich lag in
I was in bond-age, In chains of e-vil, I was in

Refrain

Lie-be, Er liebt auch mich. Drum sag ich noch ein-mal:
loved us, And loves me too. I'll sing it o'er and o'er:
Ban-den Und konnt nicht los.
bond-age Of sin and care.

Gott ist die Lie-be, Gott ist die Lie-be, Er liebt auch mich.
The won-drous sto-ry, That God so loved us, And loves me too.

3. Ee sandte Jesum, Den treuen Heiland;
Er sandte Jesum Und macht mich los.
4. Er liess mich laden, Durchs Wort der Gnaden;
Er liess mich laden Durch seinen Geist.
5. Dich will ich preisen, Du ew'ge Liebe
Dich will ich loben, So lang ich bin.

3. He sent the Savior, The blest Redeemer;
He sent the Savior To set me free.
4. He bade me welcome, O word of mercy;
He bade me welcome, O voice divine.
5. And I will praise Thee, Thou love immortal;
And I will praise Thee For ever more.

152 Peace, Perfect Peace

Edward H. Bickersteth
In rather slow time

Alt. from George J. Caldbeck
by Charles J. Vincent

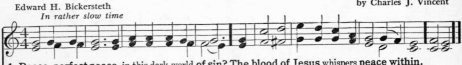

1. Peace, perfect peace, in this dark world of sin? The blood of Jesus whispers peace within.
2. Peace, perfect peace, with sorrows surging round? On Jesus' bosom naught but calm is found.
3. Peace, perfect peace, our future all unknown? Jesus we know, and He is on the throne.
4. Peace, perfect peace, death shadowing us and ours? Jesus has vanquished death and all its powers.
5. It is enough: earth's struggles soon shall cease, And Jesus call us to heaven's perfect peace. Amen.

CAROLS

153

No Room in the Inn
(Advent)

Words, Traditional

Traditional Tune
Arr. Martin Shaw

1. When Cae-sar Au-gus-tus had raised a tax-a-tion, He as-
Then Jos-eph and Ma-ry who from Da-vid did spring, Went
2. They sought en-ter-tain-ment, but none could they find, Great
Their kin-dred ac-count-ed they come were too soon; 'Too

sessed all the peo-ple that dwelt in the na-tion; The Jews at that time be-ing
up to the cit-y of Da-vid their king, And, there be-ing en-tered, cold
num-bers of strang-ers had fill-ed the inn; They knock-ed and call-ed all
late, 'said the inn-keep-er, 'here is no room.' A-mongst strang-ers and kins-folk cold

un-der Rome's sway Ap-peared in the cit-y their trib-ute to pay:
wel-come they find. From the rich to the poor they are most-ly un-kind.
this at the door, But found not a friend where in kind they had store;
wel-come they find. From the rich to the poor they are most-ly un-kind.

3. Good Joseph was troubled, but most for his dear,
   For her blessèd burden whose time now drew near;
   His heart with true sorrow was sorely afflicted
   That his virgin spouse was so rudely neglected.
   He could get no house-room who houses did frame,
   But Joseph and Mary must go as they came.
   For little is the favor the poor man can find.—
   From the rich to the poor they are mostly unkind.

4. Whilst the great and the wealthy do frolic in hall,
   Possess all the ground-rooms and chambers and all,
   Poor Joseph and Mary are thrust in a stable
   In Bethlehem city, ground inhospitáble,
   And with their mean lodging contented they be:
   For the minds of the just with their fortunes agree;
   They bear all affronts with their meekness of mind,
   And be not offended though the rich be unkind.

5. O Bethlehem, Bethlehem, welcome this stranger
   That was born in a stable and laid in a manger;
   For he is a Physician to heal all our smarts—
   Come welcome, sweet Jesus, and lodge in our hearts.

154

Infant So Gentle
(Nativity)

Traditional

Gascon Carol

1. In - fant so gen - tle, so pure and so sweet— Love from Thy
2. In - fant so ho - ly, so meek and so mild,— We come to

ti - ny eyes sin - ners doth greet, Ten-d'rest words fail all Thy
wel - come Thee, our dear Christ-child. We can - not tell Thee how

beau - ty to show— We must a - dore Thee, if Thee we would know.
much we do need,— Thy pre-cious pres-ence; all sin - ner take heed.

155

The Cradle
(Nativity)

"Ein Kindlein in der Weige"
Tr. Robert Graves

Austrian, 1649
Arr. Martin Shaw

1. He smiles with - in His cra - dle, A babe with
2. This babe we now de - clare to you Is Je - sus
3. And who would rock the cra - dle Where - in the
4. O Je - sus, dear - est babe of all And dear - est

face so bright It beams most like a mir - ror
Christ our Lord; He brings both peace and hear - ti - ness:
in - fant lies, Must rock with eas - y mo - tion
babe of mine, Thy love is great, Thy limbs are small.

From the Oxford Book of Carols. Used by permission of the Oxford University Press.

A - gainst a blaze of light: This babe so burn - ing bright.
Haste, haste with one ac - cord To feast with Christ our Lord.
And watch with hum - ble eyes, Like Ma - ry pure and wise.
O flood this heart of mine With o - ver flow from thine!

156 Rocking

(Nativity)

Czech Carol, 'Hajej, nynjej.'
Tr. O. B. C.

Arr. Martin Shaw

1. Lit - tle Je - sus, sweet-ly sleep, do not stir; We will lend a
2. Ma - ry's lit - tle ba - by, sleep, sweet-ly sleep, Sleep in com - fort

coat of fur, We will rock you, rock you, rock you, We will rock you,
slum - ber deep; We will rock you, rock you, rock you, We will rock you,

rock you, rock you: See the fur to keep you warm, Snug-ly round your ti - ny form.
rock you, rock you: We will serve you all we can, Dar-ling, dar-ling lit - tle man.

This carol may well be sung twice.
From the *Oxford Book of Carols*. Used by permission of the Oxford University Press.

157
Poverty
(Nativity)

Welsh carol
Tr. K. E. Roberts

Dr. Caradog Roberts

1. All poor men and hum-ble, All lame men who stum-ble, Come haste ye, nor
For Je-sus, our treas-ure, With love past all meas-ure, In low-ly poor

feel us a-fraid; 2. Though wise men who found Him Laid rich gifts a-
man-ger was laid. 3. Then haste we to show Him The prais-es we

round Him, Yet ox-en they gave Him their hay:
owe Him; Our ser-vice He ne'er can de-spise:

And Je-sus in beau-ty Ac-cept-ed their
Whose love still is a-ble To show us that

du-ty; Con-tent-ed in man-ger He lay.
sta-ble Where soft-ly in man-ger He lies.

158 I Saw Three Ships
(Christmas)

Traditional

Traditional
Arr. Martin Shaw

1. I saw three ships come sail-ing in,
2. And what was in those ships all three? *On Christ-mas Day, On Christ-mas Day,*
3. Our Sav-iour Christ and His La-dy.

I saw three ships come sail-ing in,
And what was in those ships all three? *On Christ-mas Day in the morn-ing.*
Our Sav-iour Christ and His la-dy.

4. Pray, whither sailed those ships all three?
5. O, they sailed into Bethlehem.
6. And all the bells on earth shall ring.
7. And all the angels in Heaven shall sing.
8. And all the souls on earth shall sing.
9. Then let us all rejoice again!

Harmony from the *Oxford Book of Carols.* Used by permission of the Oxford University Press.

159 Coventry Carol
(Christmas)

Robert Croo, 1534
Refrain

Modern version of tune
Arr. Martin Shaw
End here.

Lul-ly, lul-la, thou lit-tle ti-ny child, By by, lul-ly lul-lay.

1. O sis-ters too, How may we do, For to pre-serve this day;
2. Her-od the king, In his rag-ing, Charg-ed he hath this day;
3. That woe is me, Poor child for Thee! And ev-er morn and day,

Dal :N:

This poor young-ling, For whom we sing, By by, lul-ly lul-lay?
His men of might, In his own sight, All young chil-dren to slay.
For thy part-ing neither say nor sing By by, lul-ly lul-lay!

From The English Carol Book. Used by permission of A. R. Mowbray & Co., Ltd.
(A three-part arrangement of this carol is found at No. 184.)

While by My Sheep

(Christmas)

Seventeenth Century Carol
Arr. by Hugo Jüngst, 1853-1923; Alt.

From the German

1. While by my sheep I watched at night, Glad ti - dings
2. There shall be born, so he did say, In Beth - le -
3. There shall the Child lie in a stall, This Child who
4. This gift of God we'll cher - ish well, That ev - er

brought an an - gel bright.
hem a Child to - day; How great my joy! Great my joy!
shall re - deem us all.
joy our hearts shall fill.

Joy, joy, joy! Joy, joy, joy! Praise we the Lord in

heaven on high! Praise we the Lord in heaven on high!

161 Good Christian Men, Rejoice

(Christmas)

Anonymous, 1300
Tr. by John M. Neale, 1853

German Melody, 14th Century
Arr. John Stainer

1.–3. Good Chris-tian men, re - joice— With heart and soul and voice,—

Give ye heed to what we say: News! News! Je - sus Christ is
Now ye hear of end - less bliss: Joy! Joy! Je - sus Christ was
Now ye need not fear the grave: Peace! Peace! Je - sus Christ was

born to - day! Ox and ass be - fore Him bow, And He is in the
born for this. He hath ope'd the heav'n - ly door, And man is bless - ed
born to save. Calls you one and calls you all, To gain His ev - er -

man - ger now; Christ is born to - day!— Christ is born to - day.
ev - er - more; Christ was born for this.— Christ was born for this.
last - ing hall; Christ was born to save.— Christ was born to save.

162

Nun Ist Sie Erschienen

(Christmas)

W. Horn
Tr. H. J. L., 1954

James R. Murray

1. Nun ist sie er - schie - nen, die himm - li - sche Son - ne, Und
   Now ap - pear - eth the Heav - en - ly Sun in its glo - ry, It
2. Wie lag sie um - nach - tet in Tod und Ver - der - ben, Die
   The peo - ple that walk - ed in sin's con - dem - na - tion, And

strahlt durch die ir - di - sche Nacht; Da - rum trock - net die Thrä - nen und jauch - zet
streams thru' the dark - ness of earth; So then dry tears of sad - ness and sing the
Mensch - heit, voll Sün - de und Not! Doch durch Chris - tum kann je - der die Se - lig -
wea - ry of bat - tle and strife Now in - her - it in Je - sus the gift of

vor Won - ne; Denn den Men - schen ist Heil nun in Chri - sto ge - bracht.
glad sto - ry Of a Sav - iour now come by the heav - en - ly birth.
keit er - ben; "Glaubt und le - bet" so heist's nun ge - lo - bet sei Gott.
sal - va - tion, "Be - lieve ye and live," says the Lord of all life.

Refrain

Dem Hei - land sei Eh - re Und Frie - den der Welt
To Je - sus be glo - ry and peace on the earth
Dem Hei-land sei Eh - re, Hei-land sei Eh - re, Frie-den und Heil der Welt
To Je-sus be glo - ry, Je-sus be glo - ry, peace and good-will on earth

In Chri - sto dem Ret - ter, Ist Heil uns be - stellt
In Christ is sal - va - tion, Pro - claim we His birth.
In Chri-sto dem Ret - ter, Chri-sto dem Ret-ter, Ist Frie-den und Heil (uns) be-stellt.
In Christ is sal - va-tion, In Christ is sal-va-tion, Pro-claim we to - day His birth.

163   O du Fröhliche

(Christmas)

Johannes Daniel Falk, 1768-1826
Tr. H. J. L., 1954

Sicilian Folk Tune

1-3. O du fröh - li - che, O du se - li - ge gna-den brin - gen-de
      O thou joy - ful O thou bless - ed Grace re - veal - ing

Weih - nachts-zeit! 1. Welt ging ver - lo— ren, Christ ist ge -
Christ - mas - tide! Earth lost in dark-est night, Christ is born, the

bo - ren. 1-3. Freu - e, fru - e dich, o Chri - sten - heit!
Light of Light. Sing ye, Re - joice ye, On ev - ery side!

2. Christ ist ereschienen,
    Uns zu versühnen:

2. Christ now appearing,
    Our salvation nearing:

3. Himmlische Heere
    Jauchzen dir Ehre.

3. Heavenly hosts are singing,
    Songs of praises ringing.

164 Song of the Crib

(Christmas)

German Carol, c. 1500
Tr. N. S. T.

German Carol Melody, 14th century
Har. by R. Vaughan Williams, 1906

1. (*Mary*) "Jo - seph dear-est, Jo - seph mine, Help me cra-dle the child di - vine;
2. (*Joseph*) "Glad - ly, dear one, la - dy mine, Help I cra-dle this child of thine;

God re - ward thee and all that's thine In par - a - dise," So
God's own light on us both shall shine In par - a - dise, As

Refrain

prays the moth - er Ma - ry. He came a-mong us at Christ-mas-tide, At
prays the moth - er Ma - ry."

Christ-mas-tide, In Beth - le - hem; Men shall bring Him from far and wide Love's

di - a - dem: Je - sus, Je - sus, Lo, He comes, and loves, and saves, and frees us!

3. *Servant* (1)
Peace to all that have goodwill!
God, who heaven and earth doth fill,
Comes to turn us away from ill,
  And lies so still
    Within the crib of Mary.
      Refrain

4. *Servant* (2)
All shall come and bow the knee;
Wise and happy their souls shall be,
Loving such a divinity,
  As all may see
    In Jesus, Son of Mary.
      Refrain

5. *Servant* (3)
Now is born Emmanuel,
Prophesied once by Ezekiel,
Promised Mary by Gabriel—
  Ah, who can tell
    Thy praises, Son of Mary!
      Refrain

6. *Servant* (4)
Thou my lazy heart hast stirred,
Thou, the Father's eternal Word,
Greater than aught that ear hath heard,
  Thou tiny bird
    Of love, thou Son of Mary.
      Refrain

7. *Servant* (1)
Sweet and lovely little one,
Thou princely, beautiful, God's own Son,
Without thee all of us were undone;
  Our love is won
    By thine, O Son of Mary.
      Refrain

8. *Servant* (2)
Little man, and God indeed,
Little and poor, thou art all we need;
We will follow where thou dost lead,
  And we will heed
    Our brother, born of Mary.
      Refrain

From *The Oxford Book of Carols,* by permission of Oxford University Press.

165 Susanni

(Christmas: Epiphany)

15th Century

German Tune
Arr. Martin Shaw

1. A lit - tle child there is y - born,
2. Now Je - sus is the child-es name,
3. It fell up - on the high mid-night, Ei - a - Ei - a, su-san-ni,
4. Three kings there came with their pres-ents
5. Now sit we down up - on our knee,

su - san - ni, su - san - ni.
And He sprang out of Jes - se's thorn,
The Ma - ry mild she is his dame:
The stars they shone both fair and bright, Al -
Of myrrh and gold and frank - in - cense,
And pray we to the Trin - i - ty,

le - lu - ya, Al - le - lu - ya.
To save all us that were for - lorn.
And so our sor-row is turned to game.
The an - gels sang with all their might.
As clerk - es sang in their se-quence.
Our help, our suc - cor for to be.

From *The Oxford Book of Carols.* Used by permission of the Oxford University Press.

166 Der Tannenbaum

(Christmas)

Tr. H. J. L., 1954

German Folk Song

1. O Tan - nen-baum, O Tan - nen-baum! Wie treu sind dei - ne
   O Christ - mas tree, O Christ-mas tree! How true thy leaves will
2. O Tan - nen-baum, O Tan - nen-baum! Du kannst mir sehr ge-
   O Christ - mas tree, O Christ-mas tree! How ver - y dear thou

Blät - ter; du grünst nicht nur zur Som - mer - zeit, nein,
ev - er be; Thy ver - dure green, in sum'mer's glow, As
fal - len; Wie oft hat nicht zur Weih-nachs - zeit Ein
art to me; How oft - en thou at Christ - mas - time Hast

auch im Win - ter, wenn es schneit. O Tan - nen - baum,
in the cold of win - ter's snow. O Christ - mas tree,
Baum von dir mich hoch er - freut. O Tan - nen - baum,
filled my soul with joy di - vine. O Christ - mas tree,

O Tan - nen - baum! Wie treu sind dei - ne Blät - ter.
O Christ-mas tree! How true thy leaves will ev - er be.
O Tan - nen - baum! Du kannst mir sehr ge - fal - len.
O Christ - mas tree! How ver - y dear thou art to me.

3. O Tannenbaum, O Tannenbaum!
   Dein Kleid will mich was lehren:
   Die Hoffnung und Beständigkeit
   Giebt Trost und Kraft zu jeder Zeit.

O Christmas tree, O Christmas tree
Thy verdure speaks of life to me;
The sign of hope and constancy
My daily strength and comfort be.

167

Flemish Carol

(Christmas and New Year)

Old Flemish
Tr. R. C. Trevelyan

Traditional Flemish
Arr. Julius Röntgen

1. A lit - tle child on the earth has been born,
2. He came to earth but no home did He find,
3. He came to earth for the sake of us all,

A lit - tle child on the earth has been born;
He came to earth but no home did He find,
He came to earth for the sake of us all

He came to the earth for the sake of us all,
He came to earth and its cross did He bear,
And wish - es all a hap - py New Year,

He came to earth for the sake of us all!
He came to earth and its cross did He bear.
And wish - es all a hap - py New Year.

From *The Oxford Book of Carols.* Used by permission of the Oxford University Press.

168

Falan — Tiding

(Epiphany: Christmas)

c. 1610

Tyrolese tune
Arr. Martin Shaw

1. Out of the ori - ent crys - tal skies A blaz - ing star did shine,
2. This shin - ing star three kings did guide Even from the fur - thest East,
3. And for the joy of His great birth A thou - sand an - gels sing:

Show - ing the place where poor - ly lies A bless - ed Babe di - vine,
To Beth - le - hem where it be - tide This bless - ed Babe did rest,
"Glo - ry and peace un - to the earth Where born is this new King!"

Born of a maid of roy - al blood Who Ma - ry hight by name,
Laid in a sim - ple man - ger poor, Be - twixt an ox and ass,
The shep - herds dwell - ing there a - bout, When they this news did know,

A sa - cred rose which once did bud By grace of heaven - ly flame.
Whom these three kings did all a - dore As God's high pleas - ure was.
Came sing - ing all even in a rout, 'Fa - lan ti - ding di - do!'

169 We Three Kings of Orient Are

(CHRISTMAS: EPIPHANY)

John H. Hopkins, 1862   John H. Hopkins, 1862

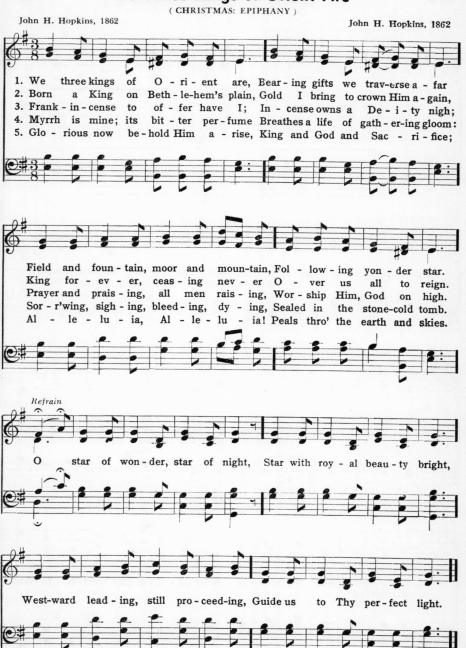

1. We   three kings   of   O - ri - ent   are, Bear - ing gifts we trav-erse a - far
2. Born   a   King   on Beth - le-hem's plain, Gold   I bring to crown Him a - gain,
3. Frank - in - cense   to   of - fer have I;   In - cense owns a   De - i - ty nigh;
4. Myrrh is mine; its bit - ter per - fume Breathes a life of gath - er-ing gloom:
5. Glo - rious now   be - hold Him   a - rise, King and God and   Sac - ri - fice;

Field and foun - tain, moor and   moun-tain, Fol - low - ing yon - der star.
King   for - ev - er, ceas - ing   nev - er O - ver us   all   to reign.
Prayer and prais - ing, all men rais - ing, Wor - ship Him, God   on high.
Sor - r'wing, sigh - ing, bleed - ing, dy - ing, Sealed in   the stone-cold tomb.
Al - le - lu - ia,   Al - le - lu - ia! Peals thro' the earth and skies.

Refrain

O   star of won - der, star of night, Star with roy - al beau - ty bright,

West-ward lead - ing, still pro - ceed-ing, Guide us   to Thy per - fect light.

170

Watts's Cradle Song
(General)

Isaac Watts
V. 1 sung as a Soprano solo unaccompanied.
V. 2, the words sung by sopranos, other parts hum accompaniment.

Northumbrian tune
freely arr. Martin Shaw

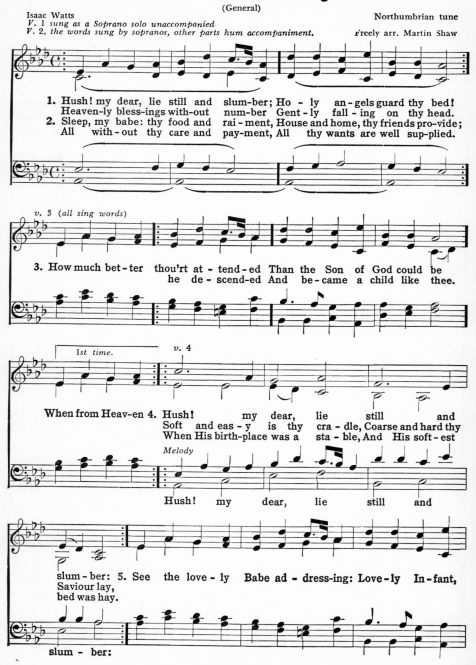

1. Hush! my dear, lie still and slum-ber; Ho - ly an - gels guard thy bed!
   Heaven-ly bless-ings with-out num-ber Gent - ly fall - ing on thy head.
2. Sleep, my babe: thy food and rai - ment, House and home, thy friends pro-vide;
   All with - out thy care and pay-ment, All thy wants are well sup-plied.

v. 3 (all sing words)

3. How much bet - ter thou'rt at - tend - ed Than the Son of God could be
   he de - scend-ed And be - came a child like thee.

1st time.   *v. 4*

When from Heav-en 4. Hush! my dear, lie still and
Soft and eas - y is thy cra - dle, Coarse and hard thy
When His birth-place was a sta - ble, And His soft - est

Melody

Hush! my dear, lie still and

slum - ber: 5. See the love - ly Babe ad - dress-ing: Love-ly In - fant,
Saviour lay,
bed was hay.

slum - ber:

From *The Oxford Book of Carols.* Used by permission of the Oxford University Press.

171 The Seven Joys of Mary

(General)

Traditional
Solo or semi-chorus

Traditional
Arr. Martin Shaw

1. The first good joy that Ma - ry had, It was the joy of one;
2. The next good joy that Ma - ry had, It was the joy of two;
3. The next good joy that Ma - ry had, It was the joy of three;

To see the joy of Je - sus Christ, When He was first her Son.
To see her own Son Je - sus Christ, To make the lame to go.
To see her own Son Je - sus Christ, To make the blind to see:

Full Chorus

When He was first her Son, good man:
To make the lame to go, good man: And bless-ed may He be,
To make the blind to see, good man:

Both Fa - ther, Son, and Ho - ly Ghost, To all e - ter - ni - ty.

4 The next good joy that Mary had,
  It was the joy of four;
To see her own son, Jesus Christ
  To read the Bible o'er:

5 The next good joy that Mary had,
  It was the joy of five;
To see her own son, Jesus Christ
  To bring the dead alive:

6 The next good joy that Mary had,
  It was the joy of six;
To see her own son, Jesus Christ
  Upon the crucifix:

7 The next good joy that Mary had,
  It was the joy of seven;
To see her own son, Jesus Christ
  To wear the crown of heaven:

From *The Oxford Book of Carols*. Used by permission of the Oxford University Press.

172 Infinite Light

(Epiphany: Lent: General: Missionary)

B. M. G.

English Traditional
Arr. Martin Shaw

Semi-Chorus.

1. The great-ness of God in His love has been shown, The light of His life on the na-tions is thrown; And that which the Jews and the Greeks did di-vine Is come in the ful-ness of Je-sus to shine: The Light of the world in the darkness has shone, And grows in our sight as the a-ges flow on.

2. He rolls the grim darkness and sor-row a-way And brings all our fears to the light of the day; The i-dols are fall-en of an-ger and blood, And God is re-vealed as the lov-ing and good:

3. And, though we have sinned like the Prod-i-gal Son, His love to our suc-cor and wel-come will run. His gos-pel of par-don, of love and ac-cord, Will mas-ter op-pres-sion and shat-ter the sword:

4. The Light of the world is more clear to our sight As er-rors dis-perse and men see Him a-right: In lands long in shad-ow, His Churches a-rise And blaze for their neigh-bors the Way of the Wise:

Full Chorus

From *The Oxford Book of Carols*. Used by permission of the Oxford University Press.

173
Now Quit Your Care

(Ash Wednesday to the Eve of Passion Sunday)

V. 1 and any other selected verses (except the last)
Soprano and alto sing the words

Angevin Tune
Arr. Martin Shaw

In moderate time

1. Now quit your care And an-xious fear and wor - ry; For schemes are vain And fret-ting brings no gain. To prayer, to prayer! Bells call and clash and hur - ry, In Lent the bells do cry, 'Come buy, come buy, Come buy with love the love most high, Come buy, come buy, Come buy with love the love most high.

The last verse and any other selected verses. (All sing the words.)
Rather quick.

6. Then shall your light Break forth as doth the morn-ing; Your health shall spring, The

friends you make shall bring God's glo - ry bright, Your way through life a - dorn - ing:

A - rise and make a par - a -

And love shall be the prize. A - rise! A - rise!

a - rise, a - rise, a -

A-rise! and make a par - a -

dise, a - rise A - rise! A - rise! A - rise! and make a par - a - dise!

dise!

2 Lent comes in the spring,
  And spring is pied with brightness;
    The sweetest flowers,
    Keen winds, and sun, and showers,
  Their health do bring
  To make Lent's chastened whiteness;
    For life to men brings light
      And might, and might,
      And might to those whose hearts are right.

3 To bow the head
  In sackcloth and in ashes,
    Or rend the soul,
    Such grief is not Lent's goal;
  But to be led
  To where God's glory flashes,
    His beauty to come nigh,
      To fly, to fly,
      To fly where truth and light do lie.

4 For is not this
  The fast that I have chosen?—
    The prophet spoke—
    To shatter every yoke,
  Of wickedness
  The grievous bands to loosen,
    Oppression put to flight,
      To fight, to fight,
      To fight till every wrong's set right.

5 For righteousness
  And peace will show their faces
    To those who feed
    The hungry in their need,
  And wrongs redress,
  Who build the old waste places,
    And in the darkness shine.
      Divine, divine,
      Divine it is when all combine!

The words are in part a paraphrase of the Lent Lesson, Isaiah 58: 1-8.
From *The Oxford Book of Carols.* Used by permission of the Oxford University Press.

174 Carol of Beauty

(General, Praise)

Steuart Wilson

French Tune
Arr. Martin Shaw

1. Praise we the Lord, who made all beau - ty For all our
2. Praise Him who makes our life a plea - sure, Send - ing us
3. Praise Him who by a sim - ple flow - er Lifts up our
4. Praise we the Lord, who made all beau - ty For all our

sens - es to en - joy; Owe we our hum - ble thanks and du - ty
things which glad our eyes; Thank Him who gives us wel-come lei - sure
hearts to things a - bove; Thank Him who gives to each one pow - er
sens - es to en - joy; Give we our hum - ble thanks and du - ty

That sim - ple pleas-ures nev - er cloy; Praise we the Lord who
That in our hearts sweet thoughts may rise; Praise Him who makes our
To find a friend to know and love; Praise Him who by a
That sim - ple plea-sures nev - er cloy; Praise we the Lord who

made all beau - ty For all our sens - es to en - joy.
life a pleas - ure Send - ing us things which glad our eyes.
sim - ple flow - er Lifts up our hearts to things a - bove.
made all beau - ty For all our sens - es to en - joy.

175 The Spirit

(Whitsuntide: General)

Geoffrey Dearmer

Angevin Tune
Arr. Martin Shaw

1. Winds of God un-fail-ing fill the sun-lit sails Of a great ship
2. If ye then per-ceive and if the heart de-sire, Shall the mind a-
3. His is each pro-fes-sion, ev-'ry man his priest Who in work's ex-

sail-ing where con-jec-ture fails: Seek-ers we, and we must dis-cov-er,
chieve, and spir-it shall as-pire; Then shall man see Him, and shall praise Him,
pres-sion finds his joy in-creased: In His church are the plow-man, sail-or,

Seek-ers we, seek-ers we,
Then shall man, then shall man,
In His church, in His church,

Doubt we not though the chart is hid—Chart we may not see, Plot-ted by the
In the fern, in the sea and cloud: Ev'-ry flower and tree In the sap of
Merc-hant, prince, ar-ti-san and clerk, And who-e'er they be, Crafts-man, thinker,

Doubt we not, Doubt we not.
In the fern, In the fern.
Mer-chant, prince, Mer-chant, prince,

world's great Lov-er Down in Gal-i-lee; Cap-tain, prince, and pi-lot He.
life must raise Him, As in Gal-i-lee In the form of man rose He.
tink-er, tail-or, Come to Gal-i-lee, Find a plan and that is He.

From *The Oxford Book of Carols.* Used by permission of the Oxford University Press.

176

Job

(General)

Words collected and arranged by Cecil J. Sharp

Traditional
Arr. Martin Shaw

1. Come all you wor - thy Chris - tian men That dwell up - on this land,
2. Now Job he was a pa - tient man, The rich - est in the East:
3. Come all you wor - thy Chris - tian men That are so ver - y poor,
4. The time, a - las, it soon will come When part - ed we shall be;

Don't spend your time in ri - ot - ing; Re - mem - ber you're but man.
When he was brought to pov - er - ty, His sor - rows soon in - creased.
Re - mem-ber how poor Laz - a - rus Lay at the rich man's door,
But all the dif - f'rence it will make Is in joy and mis - er - y;

Be watch - ful for your lat - ter end; Be read - y for your call.
He bore them all most pa - tient - ly; From sin he did re - frain;
While beg-ging of the crumbs of bread That from his ta - ble fell
And we must give a strict ac - count Of great as well as small,

There are man - y chang-es in this world; Some rise while oth-ers fall.
He al-ways trust -ed in the Lord; He soon got rich a - gain.
The Scrip-tures do in - form us all That in Heav-en he doth dwell.
Be - lieve me, now, dear Chris-tian friends, That God will judge us all.

Harmony from *Oxford Book of Carols*. Used by permission of Oxford University Press.
Words by permission of Novello and Co., Ltd.

177   Jacob's Ladder   Arr. Martin Shaw

Semi-Chorus   (General)

1. As Ja - cob with trav - el was wea - ry one day—, At night on a
2. This lad - der is long, it is strong and well - made, Has stood hundreds of
3. Come let us as - cend! all may climb it who will; For the an - gels of
4. And when we ar - rive at the ha - ven of rest, We shall hear the glad

stone for a pil - low he lay; He saw in a vi - sion a lad - der so
years and is not yet de - cayed; Man-y millions have climbed it and reached Si-on's
Jac - ob are guard-ing it still: And re-member each step that by faith we pass
words, 'Come up hith-er, ye blest, Here are re-gions of light, here are man-sions of

Full Chorus

high, That its foot was on earth and its top in the sky: Al - le - lu - ya to
hill, And thou-sands by faith are climb-ing it still:
o'er, Some proph-et or mar-tyr hath trod it be-fore;
bliss.' O, who would not climb such a lad-der as this?

Je - sus, who died on the tree, And hath raised up a lad - der of

mer - cy for me, And hath raised up a lad - der of mer - cy for me.

From *The English Carol Book*. Used by permission.

Nos Galan

(Winter: New Year)

Pr. K. E. Roberts

Welsh
Arr. Martin Shaw

1. Now the joy-ful bells a - ring-ing All ye moun-tains, praise the Lord!
2. Dear our homes as dear none oth - er; Where the moun-tains praise the Lord!
3. Cold the year, new white-ness wear-ing, All ye moun-tains praise the Lord!

Lift our hearts, like birds a - wing-ing All ye moun-tains, praise the Lord!
Glad - ly here our care we smoth - er Where the moun-tains praise the Lord!
Peace, good-will to us a - bear-ing All ye moun-tains praise the Lord!

Now our fes - tal sea - son, bring-ing Kins - men all, to bide and board,
Here we know that Christ our broth-er Binds us all as by a cord:
Now we all God's good-ness shar-ing Break the bread and sheathe the sword:

Sets our cheer - y voice a - sing-ing: All ye moun-tains, praise the Lord!
He was born of Ma - ry moth - er Where the moun-tains praise the Lord!
Bright our hearths the sig - nal flar-ing All ye moun-tains praise the Lord!

Words based on the Welsh New Year's Eve carol, Nos Galan. On New Year's Eve or Day v. 3 line 5 may be "Now we all the New Year sharing."

From The Oxford Book of Carols. Used by permission of the Oxford University Press.

179 Carol of Service

(General)

Steuart Wilson
Moderately quick

French Tune
Arr. Martin Shaw

1. Up, my neigh-bor, come a - way, See the world for us to - day,
2. Up, my neigh-bor, see the plow For our hands lies wait-ing now;
3. Up, my neigh-bor, see the land Read - y for the sow-er's hand;
4. Up, my neigh-bor, now the corn Rip - ens at the har-vest morn;
5. Up, my neigh-bor, let us pray, Thank our Mak - er ev - 'ry day,

The hands to help, the mouths to feed, The sights to see, the
Grasp well the stilt, yoke up the team, Stride out to meet the
The plow has made an e - ven tilth, The fur - rows wait the
Then let it to our sick - le yield, And pile with sheaves the
Who gave us work our strength to test And made us proud to

Refrain

books to read: Up and get us gone, to help the
morn - ing beam:
gold - en spilth:
gold - en field:
do our best:

world a - long, Up and get us gone, my neigh - bor.

From *The Oxford Book of Carols.* Used by permission of the Oxford University Press.

180

Flower Carol
(Spring, etc.)

Piae Cantiones, 1582
Tr. O. B. C.

Piae Cantiones, 1852
Arr. Martin Shaw

Verse 1

1. Spring has now un-wrapped the flowers, Day is fast re-viv-ing,
Life in all her grow-ing powers Towards the light is striv-ing:
Gone the i-ron touch of cold, Win-ter time and frost time,
Seed-lings work-ing through the mould, Now make up for lost time.

Fa-Burden for verses 2 and 4 (melody in Tenor)

2. Herb and plant that, win-ter long, Slum-bered at their lei-sure
4. Earth puts on her dress of glee; Flowers and grass-es hide her;

Now be - stir - ring, green and strong, Find in growth their pleas - ure,
We go forth in char - i - ty— Broth-ers all be - side her;

All the world with beau - ty fills, Gold and green en - hanc - ing;
For, as man this glo - ry sees In the-a-wak - ening sea - son,

Flowers make glee a-mong the hills Set the mea-dows danc - - - - ing.
Rea - son learns the heart's de-crees, Hearts are led by rea - - - - son.

Verses 3 and 5

3. Thro' each won - der of fair days God Him - self ex -
5. Praise the Mak - er, all ye saints; He with glo - ry

3. Thro' each won - der of fair days God Him -
5. Praise the Mak - er, all ye saints; He with

3. Thro' each won - der of fair days God Him - self ex -
5. Praise the Mak - er, all ye saints; He with glo - ry

From *The Oxford Book of Carols*. Used by permission of the Oxford University Press.

This Joyful Eastertide

Cowley Carol Book, 1902

CAROLS
Dutch Tune
Arr. Geoffrey Shaw

1. This joy-ful Eas-ter-tide, A - way with care and sor - - - row!
2. My flesh in hope shall rest, And for a sea-son slum - - - ber:
3. Death's flood hath lost his chill, Since Je - sus crossed the riv - - - er:

My Love, the Cru'-ci-fied, Hath sprung to life this mor - - - row.
Till trump from east to west Shall wake the dead in num - - - ber.
Lov-er of souls, from ill My pass-ing soul de-liv - - - er.

Refrain

Had Christ, that once was slain, Ne'er burst His three-day pris-on,

Our faith had been in vain: But now hath Christ a-ris-en, a-ris-en,

a-ris-en, a-ris - - - - - - en. A-men.

182
The Shepherd
(General.)

Lawrence Binyon
(*Two upper parts only sing the words*)

Austrian Tune
Arr. Martin Shaw
(*All sing the words*)

1. Down in the val-ley where sum-mer's laugh-ing beam Un-der the
2. Ah, how they strug-gle, and pant, the sil-ly sheep, Fear-ing the
3. Eve-ning is o-ver the land, with peace and light, Now sits the

wil-low tree lights a-long the stream, Shep-herds come driv-ing their flocks and
hands that dip, fear-ing wa-tery deep. Ten-der-ly lift-ed up, glad-ly,
shep-herd a-lone in eve-ning bright, Now has he joy with-in, where he

seek the pool, Plung-ing their sheep in the sun-ny wa-ter cool.
one by one, White in the green of the mead-ow, lo, they run.
pip-eth low, See-ing his flock gath-ered round him white as snow.

From *The Oxford Book of Carols*. Used by permission of the Oxford University Press.

183
It Is the Joyful Easter Time
(Easter)

A. M. Milner-Barry

Old Cornish Carol

1. It is the joy-ful East-er time, Let all sing Hal-le-lu-jah!
2. The Church is bright with flow-ers gay, And all Christ's peo-ple praise and pray,

The mer-ry bells ring out their chime, "But now hath Christ a-ris-en."
For Je-sus rose on East-er Day; Sing joy-ful Hal-le-lu-jah!

Words copyright by A.M. Milner-Barry.

184   ## Coventry Carol   S.A.A.

(Christmas)

Arr. Alvin King

Refrain

Lul - ly, Lul - la,   Thou lit - tle ti - ny child,   By, by, Lul -
Lul - ly,   Lul - la,   Lul - ly,   Lul - la,   Lul - ly,

1st. time   *End here.*

ly, lul - la.   la.
Lul - la,   lul - la   lul-la.

1. O sis - ters too, how may
2. He - rod, the king in his
3. Then woe is me, poor child

Lul - ly, lul - la, Lul -

we do   For to pre-serve this day   This poor young-ling,
rag - ing,   Charg-ed he hath this day   His men of might,
for thee!   And ev - er mourn and say,   For thy part - ing
ly,   lul - la lul - ly, lul - la, lul - ly, lul - la, lul -

After 3rd verse, sing Refrain again.

For whom we sing,   By, by, lul - ly, lul - la?
In his own sight,   All young chil-dren to slay.
Nor say nor sing   By, by, lul - ly, lul - la.
ly, lul - la, lul - ly, lul - la, lul - ly, lul - la.

185

Let Our Gladness Know no End

(Christmas)

Bohemian
Arr. Mary Oyer

1. Let our glad-ness know no end, Hal - le - lu - jah! Un - to earth did
2. See the lov'-liest bloom-ing rose, Hal - le - lu - jah! From the branch of
3. In - to flesh is made the word, Hal - le - lu - jah! 'Tis our ref - uge,

Christ de - scend, Hal - le - lu - jah!
Jes - se grows, Hal - le - lu - jah! On this day God gave us
Christ the Lord, Hal - le - lu - jah!

(Christ, His)

Christ, His Son, to save us: Christ, His Son, His Son, to save us.
(Christ to) (Christ, His)

Arrangement copyrighted. Used by permission of the composer.

186

As Lately We Watched

(Christmas)

Arr. Mary Oyer, 1954

1. As late - ly we watch'd o'er our flocks thru' the night, A star there was
2. A King of such beau - ty was ne'er be - fore seen And Ma - ry, the
3. Then Shep-herds be joy - ful, sal - ute now your King. O'er hill and o'er

seen of such glo - ri - ous light; All through the night,
moth - er, so like to a queen. Blest be the hour,
val - leys your songs now shall sing. Blest be this day,

An - gels did sing, In car - ols so sweet of the birth of a King.
Wel - come the morn, For Je - sus our Sav - iour on earth now is born.
Wel - come this morn, For Je - sus our Sav - iour on earth now is born.

Arrangement copyrighted. Used by permission of the composer.

187 Sleep, Sleep, Sleep
(Christmas)

German   Folk Song-Salzburg

Melody

Hm - - - - -

1-3. Sleep,   sleep,   sleep, dear lit - tle ba - by sleep!
     Sleep,   sleep,   sleep,   dear lit - tle ba - by

2 *Violins or Voices*

1. The an - gels now in ju - bi - la - tion, Sing-ing songs of ex - ul -
2.   Ma - ry, moth - er now ex - tol thee, Her pure heart doth now en -
3.   In the cra - dle in - fant sleep-ing, Heav'n-ly an - gels now Thee
    sleep! Ei - a po - pei - a,   Ei - a po - pei -

ta - tion, sleep, sleep, sleep dear lit - tle ba - by sleep.
fold thee.
keep - ing.
a,   sleep, sleep, sleep   dear lit - tle ba - by sleep!

Hm - - - -

From Fritz Jöde, *Der Musikant*. Translation made for this work.

188 Merry Christmas Bells

J. R. Murray

J. R. Murray

Refrain

1-2. Mer-ry, mer-ry, mer-ry, mer-ry Christ-mas bells, O sweet-ly, sweet-ly chime,

Let your hap-py mu-sic on the breez-es swell, O mer-ry, mer-ry Christ-mas time.

Duet *dolce*

1. Peace on earth, good will to men, O an - gel sing - ers, sing a - gain,
2. Ban - ish ev - 'ry thought of care, Let mirth and mu - sic fill the air,

While hearts and voic - es here be - low Send back the glad re - frain. O,
Let words of cheer and smiles a - bound, And glad-ness ev - 'ry- where. O,

Refrain

1-2. Mer-ry, mer-ry, mer-ry, mer-ry Christ-mas bells, O sweet-ly, sweet - ly chime,

Let your hap-py mu-sic on the breez-es swell, O mer-ry, mer-ry Christ-mas time.

S.S.A.A.

189   Hark, Now, O Shepherds

Old Bohemian Carol
Arr. by A. W. Stellhorn

Moderately fast, with well-marked rhythm

1. (Hark, now, O shep - herds, great news do we bring!
(Might - y the Mon - arch whose prais - es we sing.
Ding, dong, ding! Ding, dong, ding! Ding, dong, ding! Ding, dong, ding!

Ding, dong! Ding, dong! Ding, dong! Ding, dong!

Lo! in a man - ger lies Je - sus ho - ly,
Son of the gen - tle maid, Ma - ry low - ly,

rit.

a tempo   (*Use these two measures before and between the stanzas*)

Shep - herds, re - joice! Ding, dong, ding! Ding, dong, ding!

Ding, dong! Ding, dong!

pp 2 See now in beauty sweet mother and Child!
God's tender light o'er them glowing yet mild.
O'er all the world the Star, brightly beaming,
Soft sheds its loving rays, gently streaming,
Shepherds, rejoice.

mf 3 Angels bright shining, great tidings you bring,
News of sweet Mary and Jesus, our King.
Straight will we journey forth, gladly bringing
All our devotion fervently singing,
Christ now is born.

("*Kling, klang!*" *may also be used to imitate the Christmas chimes. The quarter notes may also be sung by the altos. Humming gives the effect of quietness of night. A combination of the suggestions may also be used. A. W. S.*)

S.S.A.

Come Hither, Ye Children

(Christmas)

Christian Schmidt
Tr. L. J. H., 1954

Melody, Johann Abr. Peter Schulz, 1747-1800
Arr. from Weihnachtskantate by Walter Rein

2 *violins*

Solo

(An Angel) 1. Come hith - er, ye chil - dren, O come one and

(A Child) 4. O lit - tle Lord Je - sus, what gifts can we

Violins

all, To Beth - le - hem has - ten, in man - ger so

bring, Thou best and most lov'd of all chil - dren, our

small. God's Son for a gift has been sent you this night, To

King? Thou car'st not for treas - ures and rich - es of earth, We'll

be   your Re - deem - er, your joy   and de - light.
bring Thee our hearts, and our praise   at Thy   birth.

(An Angel)

2. On   hay   and   on   straw   in   the   man - ger He   lies;
Both   Ma - ry   and   Jo - seph are   glad with sur - mise.

Small Choir of angels

The   shep-herds de - vout - ly   are kneel - ing   in   prayer, The

an - gels   a - bove   sing   their   heav - en - ly   air.

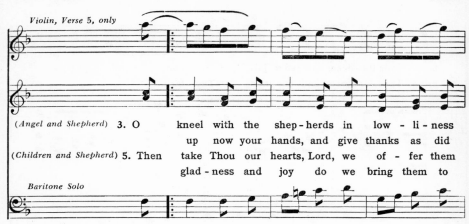

Violin, Verse 5, only

(*Angel and Shepherd*) 3. O   kneel with the   shep - herds in   low - li - ness
               up   now your   hands, and give   thanks as   did
(*Children and Shepherd*) 5. Then   take Thou our   hearts, Lord, we   of - fer them
               glad - ness and   joy   do   we   bring them to

Baritone Solo

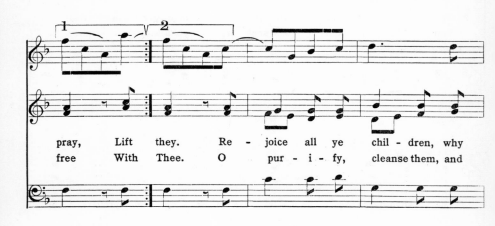

pray,   Lift   they.   Re - joice all ye   chil - dren, why
free   With   Thee.   O   pur - i - fy,   cleanse them, and

should   you   be   sad?   Sing   songs with   the   an - gels, Re-
make   us Thine   own,   And   ev - er   we'll   praise Thee, A

joice   and   be   glad.
round   Thy   great   throne.

1. Ihr Kinderlein kommet, o kommet doch all,
    Zur Krippe her kommet in Bethlehems Stall,
    Und seht, was in dieser hochleiligen Nacht
    Der Vater im Himmel für Freude uns macht.

2. Da liegt es, ihr Kinder, auf Heu und auf Stroh:
    Maria und Joseph betrachten es froh;
    Die redlichen Hirten knien betend davor,
    Hoch oben schwebt jubelnd der Engelein Chor.

3. O beugt wie die Hirten anbetend die Knie;
    Erhebet die Hände und danket wie sie!
    Stimmt freudig, ihr Kinder, wer soll sich night freun?
    Stimmt freudig zum Jubel der Engel mit ein.

4. Was geben wir Kinder, was schenken wir dir,
    Du bestes und liebstes der Kinder, dafür?
    Nichts willst du von Schätzen und Freuden der Welt,
    Ein Herz nur voll Unschuld allein dir gefällt.

5. So nimm unsre Herzen zum Opfer denn hin,
    Wir geben sie gerne mit fröhlichem Sinn,
    Und mache sie heilig und selig wie deins,
    Und mach sie auf ewig mit deinem vereint.

191 What Child Is This

Traditional
Arr. Wm. C. Dix, 1837-98

Old English Melody
Arr. O. W. M.

1. What Child is this, who, laid to rest, On Ma-ry's lap is sleep-ing,
2. Why lies He in such mean es-tate, Where ox and ass are feed-ing?
3. So bring Him in-cense, gold and myrrh, Come peas-ant, king, to own Him;

1. What child is this on Ma - ry sleep-ing?
2. He lies where ox and ass are feed-ing.
3. So bring Him gifts come all to own Him.

Whom an-gels greet with an-thems sweet, While shep-herds watch are keep-ing?
Good Chris-tian, fear: for sin-ners here The si-lent Word is plead-ing.
The King of kings sal-va-tion brings, Let lov-ing hearts en-throne Him.

The an-gels sing While shep-herds watch are keep-ing?
Good Chris-tian fear The si-lent Word is plead-ing.
The King of Kings, Let lov-ing hearts en-throne Him.

Refrain

This, this is Christ the King, whom shep-herds guard and an-gels sing:

This, this is Christ the King, whom shep-herds guard and an-gels sing:

This, this is Christ the King, The Babe, the Son of Ma - ry.

This, this is Christ the King, The Babe, the Son of Ma - ry.

192   Abide With Us, Our Saviour

Ach, bleib mit deiner Gnade

Josua Stegman, 1628   Melchior Vulpius, 1609

1. A - bide with us, our Sav - iour, Nor let Thy mer - cy cease;
2. A - bide with us, our Sav - iour, Sus - tain us by Thy word;
3. A - bide with us, our Sav - iour, Thou Light of end - less Light,

From Sa - tan's might de - fend us, And grant our soul's re - lease.
That we with all Thy peo - ple To life may be re - stored.
In - crease to us Thy bless - ings, And save us by Thy might.

193 Lo, How a Rose E'er Blooming

Es ist ein' Ros' entsprugen

Anon. 15th Century

Old German Melody
Har. Michael Praetorius, 1571-1621

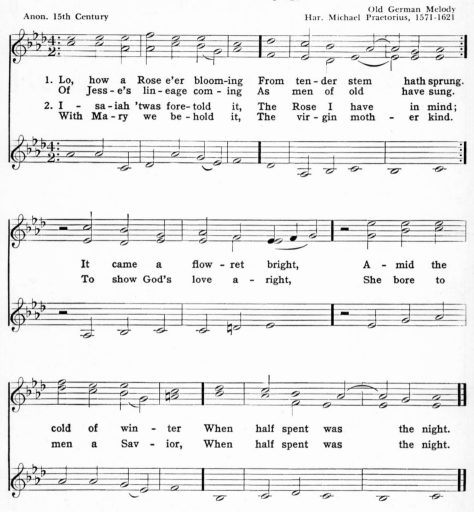

1. Lo, how a Rose e'er bloom-ing From ten-der stem hath sprung.
Of Jess-e's lin-eage com-ing As men of old have sung.

2. I-sa-iah 'twas fore-told it, The Rose I have in mind;
With Ma-ry we be-hold it, The vir-gin moth-er kind.

It came a flow-ret bright, A-mid the
To show God's love a-right, She bore to

cold of win-ter When half spent was the night.
men a Sav-ior, When half spent was the night.

1 Es ist ein' Ros' entsprungen
  Aus einer Wurzel zart,
  Als uns die Alten sungen:
  Aus Jesse kam die Art;
  Und hat ein Blümlein bracht,
  Mitten im kalten Winter,
  Wohl zu der halben Nacht.

2 Das Röslein, das ich meine,
  Davon Jesaias sagt,
  Ist Maria die reine,
  Die uns das Blümlein bracht;
  Aus Gottes ew' gem Rat
  Hat sie ein Kind geboren,
  Und blieb ein reine Magd.

194 Hail the Day That Sees Him Rise

(Easter)

Charles Wesley, 1707-1788

Robert Williams, 1817

1. Hail the day that sees Him rise, Hal - - le - lu - jah!
2. There the glo - rious tri - umph waits: Hal - - le - lu - jah!
3. See, He lifts His hands a - bove! Hal - - le - lu - jah!
4. There we shall with Thee re - main! Hal - - le - lu - jah!

Rav - ished from our wish - ful eyes! Hal - - le - lu - jah!
Lift your heads, e - ter - nal gates, Hal - - le - lu - jah!
See, He shows the prints of love! Hal - - le - lu - jah!
Part - ners of Thy end - less reign! Hal - - le - lu - jah!

Christ, a - while to mor - tals giv'n, Hal - - le - lu - jah!
Wide un - fold the ra - diant scene, Hal - - le - lu - jah!
Hark! his gra - cious lips be - stow, Hal - - le - lu - jah!
There Thy face un - cloud - ed see, Hal - - le - lu - jah!

Re - as - cends His na - tive heav'n. Hal - - le - lu - jah!
Take the King of Glo - ry in! Hal - - le - lu - jah!
Bless - ings on His Church be - low. Hal - - le - lu - jah!
Find our heav'n of heav'ns in Thee! Hal - - le - lu - jah!

195 Chime Music

(Christmas)

Tr. from the French

Old French Carol
Arr. for this work

1. Hark, the gold-en chimes for Christ-mas morn! Hark the mu-sic
2. Hark, the chil-dren's voic-es gay-ly sound! Hark the car-ols

1. Hark, the gold-en chimes for Christ-mas morn! Hark the
2. Hark, the chil-dren's voic-es gay-ly sound! Hark the

1. Hark the gold-en chimes for Christ-mas morn!
2. Hark the chil-dren's voic-es gay-ly sound!

heav-en born. Hark the tune-ful bells a-cross the snow!
all a-round. Hark! the sil-v'ry sleigh bells on the air,

mu-sic heav-en born. Hark the tune-ful bells a-cross the
car-ols all a-round. Hark! the sil-v'ry sleigh bells on the

Hark the mu-sic heav-en born. Hark the tune-ful bells a-
Hark the car-ols all a-round. Hark the sil-v'ry sleigh bells

Hark 'tis joy for all be-low. low.
Hark the laugh-ter ev-'ry where. where.

snow! Hark 'tis joy for all be-low. low.
air, Hark the laugh-ter ev-'ry where. where.

cross the snow! Hark 'tis joy for all be-low. low.
on the air, Hark the laugh-ter ev-'ry-where. where.

Refrain

Ring-dong, ding-dong, ring-dong, "Peace, good will tow'rd men!"

Ring! Ding-dong, ding-dong, "Peace, good will tow'rd men!" O hark!

Ring - dong, ding - dong, ding-dong, "Peace, good will tow'rd men!" O hark!

196 Saviour, Hear Us, We Pray

Johannes Brahms, 1833-1897

2 parts

1. Sav - iour hear us we pray, Keep us safe thru' this day;
2. Be our Guard - ian and Guide; May we walk by Thy side

Keep our lives free from sin and our hearts pure with - in.
Till the eve - ning shades fall o - ver us, o - ver all.

Refrain (3 parts)

Je - sus, Lord, hear our prayer, May we rest in Thy care;

Je - sus, Lord, hear our prayer, May we rest in Thy care.

Wiegenlied

1. Guten Abend, gut' Nacht! mit Rosen bedacht,
   Mit Näglein besteckt, schlup unter die Deck.
   Refrain: Morgen früh, wenn Gott will, wirst du wieder geweckt:

2. Guten Abend, gut' Nacht! von Englein bewacht
   Die Zeigen im Traum dir Christkindleins Baum.
   Refrain: Schlaf nur selig and süss, schau im Traum's Paradies!:

S.S.A.

197 Father, Come to Me

M. Teresa Armitage

L. S. Cherubini, 1760-1842
Arranged by J. Remington

1. Soft - ly, sweet - ly falls the night, Slow - ly, gent - ly veils the light;
2. Let Thy spir - it on us fall, Fa - ther, Fa - ther, guard us all.

God of all, Thy chil - dren keep Safe, Lord, in ho - ly sleep. Come, O,
Grant us slum - ber, free from fear, Safe, Lord, till morn ap - pear. Come, O,

come to a heart sore - ly press'd! Come, O, come to a soul that seeks
come to Thy chil - dren in need! Hear, O, hear, gen - tle Fa - ther, and

rest! Lov - ing Fa - ther, come to me, To - night, to - night, O,
heed! Lov - ing Fa - ther, come to me, To - night, to - night, O,

come to me, Fa - ther, come to me, Fa - ther, come to me!

come to me, come to me!

An Evening Hymn

E. Jonas
From the Opera "Les Infants Prodiges"

1. Fa - ther, Whose hand for bird and blos - som car - eth,
2. Bless those we love, O Lord; be still be - side them

Thou, by Whose power the stars their path - way keep,
By night or day, by land or on the deep!

Watch o'er Thy chil - dren while the shad - ows length - en,
O, in this hour draw near to all who need Thee;

Be near this night and bless us while we sleep.
Give joy for weep - ing; Bid the wea - ry sleep.

199 The Evening Bells

M. Louise Baum

Franz Abt

1. The eve - ning bells are call - ing To still the toil of day,
2. The stars be - gin to wan - der A - cross the az - ure heights;
3. Se - rene the moon comes soar - ing A - bove the si - lent wold;

And soft - lier yet is fall - ing The sun - set's mel - low ray.
From shin - ing deeps up yon - der They draw their faith - ful lights.
A - cross the dark - ness pour - ing Her ra - diant roy - al gold.

On wings of peace the dark draws nigh, To hide out earth from
They say our Fa - ther reigns a - bove And calls our hearts to—
So o'er our dark - est hour shall rise Pure peace and sol - ace

of peace the
our Fa - ther
our dark - est

Heav - en's eye; Yet safe in God's own sight Shall rest the bless - ed
Him in love; His ten - der care shall keep His chil - dren while they
from the skies; For oh, with God's own light Shall shine the bless - ed

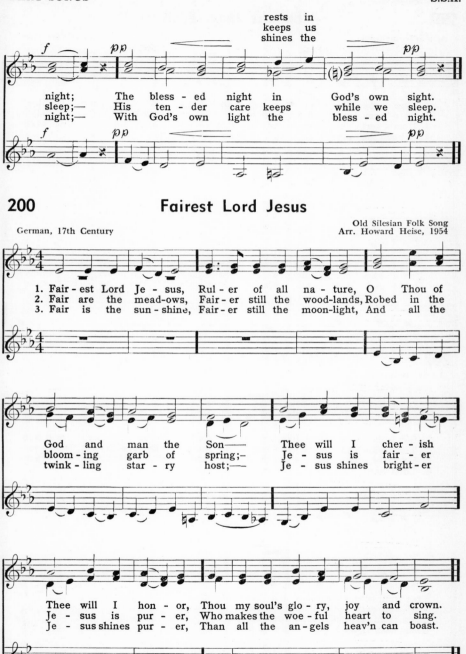

rests in
keeps us
shines the

night; The bless - ed night in God's own sight.
sleep;— His ten - der care keeps while we sleep.
night;— With God's own light the bless - ed night.

200   Fairest Lord Jesus

German, 17th Century

Old Silesian Folk Song
Arr. Howard Heise, 1954

1. Fair - est Lord Je - sus, Rul - er of all na - ture, O Thou of
2. Fair are the mead-ows, Fair - er still the wood-lands, Robed in the
3. Fair is the sun - shine, Fair - er still the moon-light, And all the

God and man the Son—— Thee will I cher - ish
bloom - ing garb of spring;– Je - sus is fair - er
twink - ling star - ry host;—— Je - sus shines bright - er

Thee will I hon - or, Thou my soul's glo - ry, joy and crown.
Je - sus is pur - er, Who makes the woe - ful heart to sing.
Je - sus shines pur - er, Than all the an - gels heav'n can boast.

201

Now the Day Is Over

Sabine Baring-Gould

Joseph Barnby

mf

1. Now the day is o - ver, Night is draw - ing nigh,
2. Je - sus, give the wea - ry Calm and sweet re - pose;
3. Com - fort ev - ery suf - ferer Watch - ing late in pain;
4. When the morn - ing wak - ens, Then may I a - rise

dim.

Shad - ows of the eve - ning Steal a - cross the sky.
With Thy ten - derest bless - ing May mine eye - lids close.
Those who plan some e - vil From their sin re - strain
Pure, and fresh, and sin - less In Thy ho - ly eyes.

dim.

pp

202

Softly Now the Light of Day

G. W. Doane

Weber

1. Soft - ly now the light of day Fades up - on my sight a - way:
2. Thou, whose all per - vad - ing eye Naught es-capes, with - out, with - in,
3. Soon, for me, the light of day Shall for - ev - er pass a - way:
4. Thou who, sin - less, yet hast known All of man's in - firm - i - ty;

Free from care, from la - bor free, Lord, I would com-mune with Thee.
Par - don each in - firm - i - ty, O - pen fault, and se - cret sin.
Then, from sin and sor - row free, Take me, Lord, to dwell with Thee.
Then, from Thine e - ter - nal throne, Je - sus, look with pity - ing eye.

203 Like As a Father

(Three-part Round)

Psalm 103: 13

Luigi Cherubini, 1760-1842

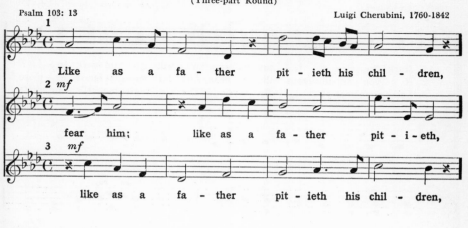

Like as a fa - ther pit - ieth his chil - dren,

2 *mf*

fear him; like as a fa - ther pit - i - eth,

3 *mf*

like as a fa - ther pit - ieth his chil - dren,

So the Lord hath mer - cy, so the Lord hath mer - cy,

pit - ieth his chil - dren, the Lord hath mer - cy,

so the Lord hath mer - cy, the Lord hath

so the Lord hath mer - cy on them that *fear, on them that

*fear him.

the Lord hath mer - cy on them that fear him;

mer - cy on them . . . . . that fear him.

*Last time.

204 Hark! the Voice of Jesus Calling

Daniel Marsh, 1868

Wolfgang Amadeus Mozart, 1756-1791

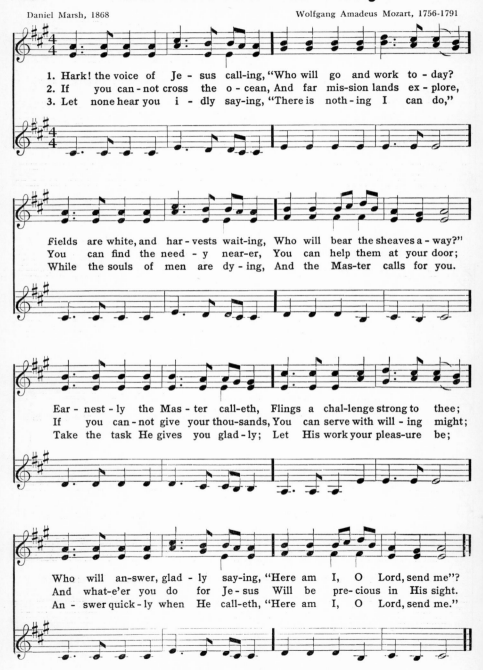

1. Hark! the voice of Je - sus call-ing, "Who will go and work to - day?
2. If you can - not cross the o - cean, And far mis-sion lands ex - plore,
3. Let none hear you i - dly say-ing, "There is noth-ing I can do,"

Fields are white, and har - vests wait-ing, Who will bear the sheaves a - way?"
You can find the need - y near-er, You can help them at your door;
While the souls of men are dy - ing, And the Mas-ter calls for you.

Ear - nest-ly the Mas - ter call-eth, Flings a chal-lenge strong to thee;
If you can - not give your thou-sands, You can serve with will - ing might;
Take the task He gives you glad - ly; Let His work your pleas-ure be;

Who will an-swer, glad - ly say-ing, "Here am I, O Lord, send me"?
And what-e'er you do for Je - sus Will be pre - cious in His sight.
An - swer quick - ly when He call-eth, "Here am I, O Lord, send me."

205 My Faith Looks Up to Thee

Ray Palmer   Lowell Mason

1. My faith looks up to Thee, Thou Lamb of Cal - va - ry,
2. May Thy rich grace im - part Strength to my faint - ing heart,
3. While life's dark maze I tread, And griefs a - round me spread,
4. When ends life's tran - sient dream, When death's cold sul - len stream

Sav - iour di - vine! Now hear me while I pray, Take all my
My zeal in - spire; As Thou hast died for me Oh, may my
Be Thou my guide, Bid dark-ness turn to day, Wipe sor - row's
Shall o'er me roll, Blest Sav-iour, then, in love Fear and dis -

guilt a - way; Oh, let me from this day Be whol - ly Thine!
love to Thee Pure, warm, and change-less be, A liv - ing fire!
tears a - way, Nor let me ev - er stray From Thee a - side.
trust re - move; Oh, bear me safe a - bove, A ran - somed soul!

O Savior, Hear Me

Christoph von Gluck, 1714-1787
Arr. Mary Oyer, 1954

Anon.

O Sav-ior, hear me, I im-plore Thee, In Thee a - lone can peace be found.
Thou canst sus-tain and Thou re - store me, What-e'er the cares that hov-er 'round.

O Sav-ior, hear me, I im - plore Thee, In Thee a - lone can peace be found.
Thou canst sus-stain and Thou re - store me, What-e'er the cares that hov-er 'round.

Hum——— Hum——— Hum———

Hear my sup-pli - ca - tion, Hum——————— Turn on me Thy

Hum——— Hear my sup-pli - ca - tion, Hum———

Hum——— Hum——————— Lord I long for

lov - ing eyes, O turn on me Thy lov - ing eyes. Lord I long for

Hum——— Hum———

The arrangement was made for this work and is copyrighted.

Thy sal - va - tion, And would fain at - tain the prize.

Thy sal - va - tion, And would fain at - tain the prize.

207 Jesus, While Living, Jesus, While Dying

Old German Melody

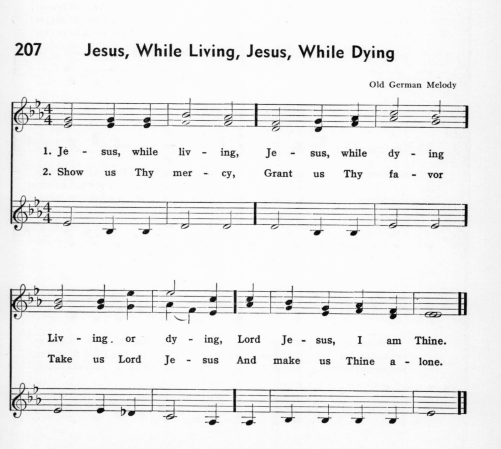

1. Je - sus, while liv - ing, Je - sus, while dy - ing
2. Show us Thy mer - cy, Grant us Thy fa - vor

Liv - ing . or dy - ing, Lord Je - sus, I am Thine.
Take us Lord Je - sus And make us Thine a - lone.

208 What a Friend We Have in Jesus

Joseph Scriven

Charles C. Converse

1. What a friend we have in Je - sus, All our sins and griefs to bear;
2. Have we tri - als and temp - ta - tions? Is there trou-ble an - y-where?
3. Are we weak and heav - y la - den, Cum-bered with a load of care?

What a priv - i - lege to car - ry Ev - 'ry-thing to God in prayer!
We should nev - er be dis - cour-aged: Take it to the Lord in prayer!
Pre - cious Sav-iour, still our ref - uge; Take it to the Lord in prayer!

O what peace we oft - en for - feit, O what need-less pain we bear,
Can we find a friend so faith - ful, Who will all our sor-rows share?
Do thy friends de-spise for-sake thee? Take it to the Lord in prayer!

All be-cause we do not car - ry Ev - 'ry-thing to God in prayer.
Je - sus knows our ev - 'ry weak-ness; Take it to the Lord in prayer!
In His arms He'll take and shield thee, Thou wilt find a sol-ace there.

209

Holy, Holy, Holy

SANCTUS

Johann Philipp Neumann, 1744-1849

Franz Schubert, 1797-1828

1. Ho - ly, ho - ly, ho - ly, Ho - ly is the Lord—
2. Ho - ly, ho - ly, ho - ly, Ho - ly is the Lord—
Hei - lig, hei - lig, hei - lig, hei - lig ist der Herr!—

Ho - ly, Ho - ly, Ho - ly, Ho - ly is He!——
Ho - ly, Ho - ly, Ho - ly, Ho - ly is He!——
Hei - lig, hei - lig, hei - lig, hei - lig ist nur Er!—

He who ne'er be - gan—— He who ev - er was—
Pow - er, won - der, love—— Round a - bout His throne!-
All - macht, Wun - der, Lie - be, al - les rings um - her,——

Ev - er is and rul - eth, Shall be ev - er more!—
Ho - ly, Ho - ly, Ho - ly, Ho - ly He a - lone!——
Hei - lig, hei - lig, hei - lig, hei - lig ist der Herr.——

The Lord's My Shepherd

BROTHER JAMES' AIR

Traditional
Arr. Rosella Reimer Duerksen

Psalm 23

1. The Lord's my Shep-herd, I'll not want, He makes me down to lie In pas-tures
2. My soul He doth re - store a-gain, And me to walk doth make With-in the

1. The Lord's my Shepherd, I'll not want, He makes me down to lie In pas-tures
2. My soul He doth re - store a - gain, And me to walk doth make With-in the

green. He lead-eth me The qui-et wa-ters by. He lead-eth me, He
Paths of Bless-ed-ness, E'en for his own Name's sake. With - in the Paths of

green. He lead-eth me The qui-et wa-ters by. He lead-eth me, He
Paths of Bless-ed-ness, E'en for his own Name's sake. With - in the Paths of

lead - eth me, the qui-et wa-ters by. 3. Yea, though I pass thro' shad-owed vale,
Blessedness, E'en for his own Name's sake. 4. My ta-ble Thou hast fur-nish - ed

lead-eth me, the qui-et wa-ters by.
Blessedness, E'en for his own Name's sake.

Yea, though I pass
My ta - ble Thou

Yet will I fear no ill;   For Thou art with me, And Thy Rod and Staff me
In pres-ence of my foes;   My head with oil Thou dost a-noint, And my cup

Melody

Yea, though I pass thro' shadowed vale, Yet will I fear no ill;   For Thou art
My   ta-ble Thou hast fur-nish-ed In pres-ence of my foes;   My head with

thro' shadowed vale I'll fear not   For Thou art with me Thy rod and
hast fur-nish-ed be-fore my foes   My head with oil Thou dost a -

com - fort still.   Thy Rod and Staff me com-fort still, me com - fort
o - ver-flows.   My head Thou dost with oil a-noint, And my cup o - ver -

with me, And Thy Rod and Staff me com-fort still.   Thy Rod and Staff me
oil   Thou dost a-noint, And my cup o - ver-flows.   My head Thou dost with

staff me com-fort still. For Thou art with me and Thy rod and Staff me comfort
noint, My cup o'er - flows. My head with oil Thou dost a-noint, and my cup o - ver -

Descant

still.   5. Good-ness and mer - cy Will
flows.

Melody

com-fort still, me com - fort still. 5. Goodness and mercy all my days Will
oil   a-noint, And my cup o - ver-flows.

still, me com-fort still.
flows, my cup o'er-flows.

sure-ly fol - low, fol-low me; In my fa-ther's heart
sure-ly fol - low me;   And in my Fa-ther's heart al - way

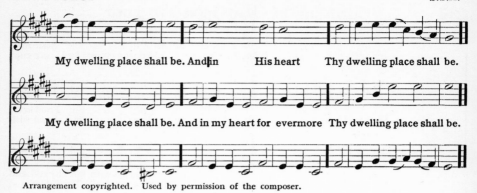

My dwelling place shall be. And in His heart Thy dwelling place shall be.

My dwelling place shall be. And in my heart for evermore Thy dwelling place shall be.

Arrangement copyrighted. Used by permission of the composer.

211   God Be Our Guide

From the German   Franz Abt

1. God be our guide, His help is sure; In Him our hope shall
2. Work that we pur - pose ev - 'ry hour Can pros - per on - ly
3. Might-y to bless from day to day, Till life's brief light shall

rest se - cure; His strength a - lone suc-cess can bring; This prayer from
through His power; Our souls His gra - cious pres-ence seek; With joy - ful
pass a - way. He gives and takes and works His will; We pray, and

ev - 'ry heart shall spring, God be our guide, God be our guide.
lips this prayer we speak, God be our guide, God be our guide.
bid our hearts be still, God be our guide, God be our guide.

212 Cast Thy Burden Upon the Lord

From "Elijah"

Felix Mendelssohn

Cast thy bur-den up-on the Lord; And He shall sus-

tain thee; He nev-er will suf-fer the right-eous to fall,

He is at thy right hand. Thy mer-cy, Lord, is

great, And far a-bove the heavens, Let none be

made a-sham-ed, That wait up-on Thee.

213 We Gather Together

Anonymous, 1625

Traditional Netherlands Melody

1. We gath - er to - geth - er to ask the Lord's bless - ing;
2. Be - side us to guide us, our God with us join - ing,
3. We all do ex - tol Thee, Thou lead - er tri - umph - ant,

He chast - ens and hast - ens His will to make known; The
Or - dain - ing, main - tain - ing His King - dom di - vine; So
And pray that Thou still our de - fend - er wilt be. Let

wick - ed op - press - ing now cease from dis-tress - ing: Sing prais - es
from the be - gin - ning the fight we were win - ning: Thou, Lord, wast
Thy con - gre - ga - tion es - cape trib - u - la - tion: Thy Name be

Alternative Ending—v. 3.

to His Name; He for - gets not His own.
at our side: all glo - ry be thine!
ev - er praised! O Lord, make us free. Lord make us free.

1 Wir treten mit Beten vor Gott, den Gerechten,
  Er waltet und haltet ein strenges Gericht,
  Er lässt von den Schlechten nicht die Guten knechten,
  Sein Name sei gelobt, er vergisst unser nicht.

2 Im Streite zur Seite ist Gott uns gestanden,
  Er wollte, es sollte das Recht siegreich sein,
  Da ward, kaum begonnen, die Schlacht schon gewonnen,
  Du Gott warst ja mit uns, der Sieg, er war dein.

3 Wir loben dich, oben, du Lenker der Schlachten,
  Und flehen mög'st stehen uns fernerhin bei,
  Dass deine Gemeinde nich Opfer der Feinde.
  Dein Name sei gelobt, o Herr, mach' uns frei!

214 Take My Life and Let It Be

Frances R. Havergal   Cesar Malan

1. Take my life and let it be Con-se-crat-ed
2. Take my feet and let them be Swift and beau-ti-
3. Take my sil-ver and my gold, Not a mite would
4. Take my lips and let them be Filled with mes-sag-
5. Take my will and make it Thine; It shall be no

Lord to Thee; Take my hands and let them move At the
ful for Thee; Take my voice, and let me sing Al-ways
I with-hold; Take my mo-ments and my days, Let them
es for Thee; Take my in-tel-lect, and use Ev-'ry
long-er mine; Take my heart, it is Thine own! It shall

im-pulse of Thy love, At the im-pulse of Thy love.
on-ly for my King, Al-ways on-ly for my King.
flow in end-less praise, Let them flow in end-less praise.
power as Thou shalt choose, Ev-'ry power as Thou shalt choose.
be Thy roy-al throne, It shall be Thy roy-al throne.

215 Savior, Like a Shepherd Lead Us

Dorothy A. Thrupp, 1838

Wm. B. Bradbury

1. Sav - ior, like a shep-herd lead us, Much we need Thy ten-d'rest care;
2. We are Thine, do Thou be - friend us, Be the guard-ian of our way;
3. Thou hast prom-ised to re - ceive us, Poor and sin - ful tho' we be;
4. Ear - ly let us seek Thy fav - or, Ear - ly let us do Thy will;

In Thy pleas-ant pas-tures feed us, For our use Thy folds pre-pare;
Keep Thy flock, from sin de - fend us, Seek us when we go a - stray;
Thou hast mer - cy to re - lieve us, Grace to cleanse, and pow'r to free:
Bless-ed Lord and on - ly Sav - ior, With Thy love our bos-oms fill:

Bless-ed Je - sus! Bless-ed Je - sus! Thou hast bought us, Thine we are,
Bless-ed Je - sus! Bless-ed Je - sus! Hear, O hear us, when we pray,
Bless-ed Je - sus! Bless-ed Je - sus! We will ear - ly turn to Thee,
Bless-ed Je - sus! Bless-ed Je - sus! Thou hast loved us, love us still,

Bless-ed Je - sus! Bless-ed Je - sus! Thou hast bought us, Thine we are.
Bless-ed Je - sus! Bless-ed Je - sus! Hear, O hear us, when we pray.
Bless-ed Je - sus! Bless-ed Je - sus! We will ear - ly turn to Thee.
Bless-ed Je - sus! Bless-ed Je - sus! Thou hast loved us, love us still.

216 Let All the World in Every Corner Sing

George Herbert, 1593-1633   Harvey Worthington Loomis

Let all the world in ev - 'ry cor - ner sing, My God and King!
In ev - 'ry cor - ner sing,
Oh sing, My God and King!

1. The heav'ns are not too high, His praise may thith-er fly;
2. The church with psalms must shout, No door may keep them out;

My God and King! My God and King!

The earth is not too low, His prais - es there may grow.
But a - bove all, the heart Must bear the long - est part.

My God and King! My God and King!

Let all the world in ev - 'ry cor-ner sing, My God and King!
In ev - 'ry cor-ner sing,

Oh, sing, My God-and- King!

217 Deck Thyself, My Soul

Johann Franck, 1649
Tr. Catherine Winkworth, 1829-78

Johann Crüger, 1649
Harmonized by Johann Sebastian Bach

1. Deck thy-self, my soul, with glad-ness, Leave the gloom-y haunts of sad-ness;
2. Sun, who all my life dost bright-en; Light, who dost my soul en-light-en;

Come in-to the day-light's splen-dor, There with joy Thy prais-es ren-der
Joy, the sweet-est man e'er know-eth; Fount, whence all my be-ing flow-eth:

Un-to Him whose grace un-bound-ed Hath this glo-rious ban-quet found-ed.
At Thy feet I cry, my Mak-er, Let me be a fit par-tak-er

High o'er all the heav'ns He reign-eth, Yet to dwell with thee He deign-eth.
Of this bless-ed food from heav-en, For our good, Thy glo-ry, giv-en.

218 Faith of Our Fathers

F. W. Faber

H. F. Hemy

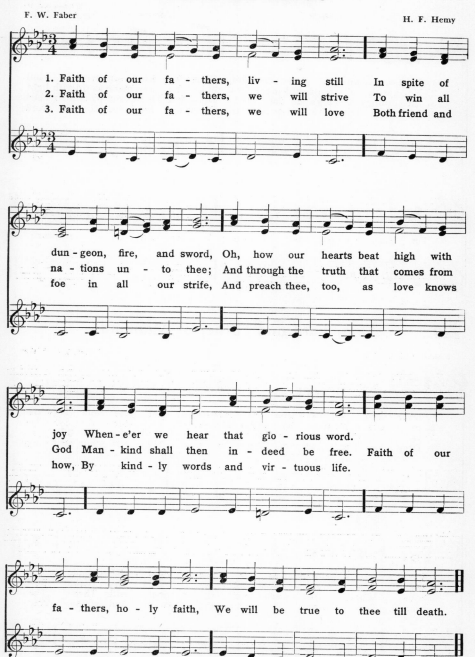

1. Faith of our fa - thers, liv - ing still In spite of
2. Faith of our fa - thers, we will strive To win all
3. Faith of our fa - thers, we will love Both friend and

dun - geon, fire, and sword, Oh, how our hearts beat high with
na - tions un - to thee; And through the truth that comes from
foe in all our strife, And preach thee, too, as love knows

joy When - e'er we hear that glo - rious word.
God Man - kind shall then in - deed be free. Faith of our
how, By kind - ly words and vir - tuous life.

fa - thers, ho - ly faith, We will be true to thee till death.

219 Let Us, With a Gladsome Mind

John Milton

Harmonized by
Franz Silcher

1. Let us, with a glad-some mind, Praise the Lord, for He is kind;
2. He, with all-com-mand-ing might, Filled the new made world with light.
3. All things liv-ing He doth feed; His full hand sup-plies their need.
4. Let us, then, with glad-some mind, Praise the Lord, for He is kind;

For His mer-cies shall en-dure, Ev-er faith-ful, ev-er sure.

220 Dear Lord and Father of Mankind

John Greenleaf Whittier

Frederick C. Maker

1. Dear Lord and Fa-ther of man-kind, For-give our fev-'rish
2. In sim-ple trust like theirs who heard, Be-side the Syr-ian
3. O Sab-bath rest by Gal-i-lee! O calm of hills a-
4. Drop Thy still dews of qui-et-ness Till all our striv-ings

ways! Re-clothe us in our right-ful mind, In
sea, The gra-cious call-ing of the Lord, Let
bove, Where Je-sus knelt the share with Thee The
cease; Take from our souls the strain and stress, And

pur - er lives Thy ser - vice find, In deep - er rev-'rence praise.
us, like them, with - out a word Rise up and fol - low Thee.
si - lence of e - ter - ni - ty, In - ter - pret - ed by love.
let our or - dered lives con - fess The beau - ty of Thy peace.

221   Jesus Shall Reign

Isaac Watts, 1719   John Hatton, c. 1793

1. Je - sus shall reign wher - e'er the sun Does his suc -
2. To Him shall end - less prayer be made, And prais - es
3. Peo - ple and realms of ev - 'ry tongue Dwell on His

ces - sive jour - neys run; His king - dom spread from
throng to crown His head; His name like sweet per -
love with sweet - est song; And in - fant voic - es

shore to shore, Till moons shall wax and wane no more.
fume, shall rise With ev - 'ry morn - ing sac - ri - fice.
shall pro - claim Their ear - ly bless - ings on His name.

4. Blessings abound where'r He reigns;
   The prisoner leaps to lose his chains,
   The weary find eternal rest,
   And all the sons of want are blest.

5. Let ev'ry creature rise and bring
   Peculiar honors, to our King;
   Angels descend with songs again,
   And earth repeat the loud Amen!

222 The Lord Is Great

Nancy Byrd Turner

Ludwig van Beethoven

1. The Lord is great, and great His end - less glo - ry,
2. The Lord is kind, His watch - ful love up - holds us,
3. The Lord is near, a change - less Friend and Giv - er,

Earth and the skies pro - claim His won-drous sto - ry;
All through our life His faith - ful - ness en - folds us;
His chil - dren know He will be with them ev - er.

He shines up - on the deep - est night,
The road is safe when by His side;
He gives us joy, He makes us strong.

No dark - ness there, for God is Light.
We can - not stray, with God for guide.
Our strength is God, and God our song!

223 Come, Ye Thankful People, Come

Stanzas 1, 2, Henry Alford
Stanza 3, Anna L. Barbauld

George J. Elvey

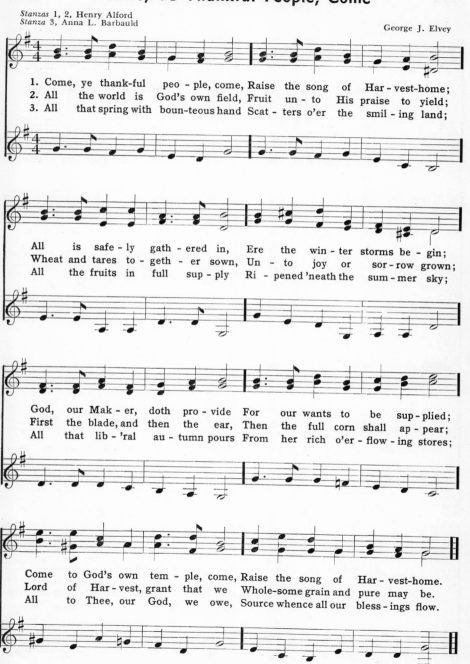

1. Come, ye thank-ful peo - ple, come, Raise the song of Har - vest-home;
2. All the world is God's own field, Fruit un - to His praise to yield;
3. All that spring with boun-teous hand Scat - ters o'er the smil - ing land;

All is safe - ly gath - ered in, Ere the win - ter storms be - gin;
Wheat and tares to - geth - er sown, Un - to joy or sor - row grown;
All the fruits in full sup - ply Ri - pened 'neath the sum - mer sky;

God, our Mak - er, doth pro - vide For our wants to be sup - plied;
First the blade, and then the ear, Then the full corn shall ap - pear;
All that lib - 'ral au - tumn pours From her rich o'er - flow - ing stores;

Come to God's own tem - ple, come, Raise the song of Har - vest-home.
Lord of Har - vest, grant that we Whole-some grain and pure may be.
All to Thee, our God, we owe, Source whence all our bless - ings flow.

224 Praise to the Lord

Joachim Neander, 1680
Tr. Catherine Winkworth

"Stralsund Gesangbuch" 1665
Arr. Samuel Burkhard

1. Praise to the Lord, the Al-might-y, the King of cre-a-tion!

O my soul, praise Him, for He is thy health and sal-va-tion!

All ye who hear, Now to His tem-ple draw near; Praise Him in

glad ad-o-ra-tion! 2. Praise to the Lord, who o'er all things so
Praise to the Lord who

won-drous-ly reign - eth, Shel-ters thee un-der His wings, yea, so
Shel-ters thee, yea, so

gent-ly sus-tain - eth! Hast thou not seen How thy en-treat-ies have
gent-ly sus-tain - eth! Hast thou not, hast thou not seen How thy

Praise to the Lord

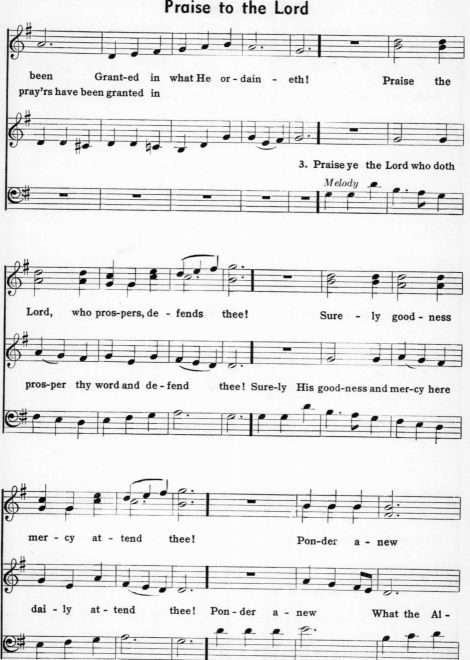

Praise to the Lord

Praise to the Lord

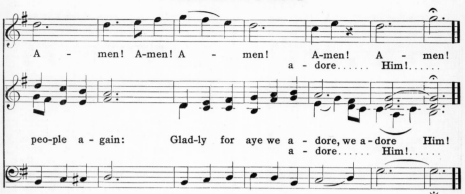

A - men! A-men! A - men!   A-men!   A - men!
                                a - dore...... Him!......

peo-ple a - gain: Glad-ly for aye we a - dore, we a - dore   Him!
                                    a - dore...... Him!......

225   Come, Thou Almighty King   S.A.A.

Charles Wesley, 1757   Felice De Giardini, 1769

1. Come, Thou Al - might - y King, Help us Thy name to sing,
2. Come, Thou In - car - nate Word, Gird on Thy might - y sword,
3. Come, Ho - ly Com - fort - er, Thy sa - cred wit - ness bear
4. To the great One in Three E - ter - nal prais - es be

Help us to praise: Fa - ther all glo - ri - ous, O'er all vic -
Our prayer at - tend: Come, and Thy peo - ple bless, And give Thy
In this glad hour: Thou who Al - might - y art, Now rule in
Hence ev - er - more. His sov - ereign maj - es - ty May we in

to - ri - ous, Come, and reign o - ver us, An - cient of Days.
word suc - cess; Spir - it of ho - li - ness On us de - scend.
ev - 'ry heart, And ne'er from us de - part, Spir - it of power.
glo - ry see And to e - ter - ni - ty Love and a - dore.

226

Praise Ye the Lord

Cecil Cowdrey

Polish Folk Song

1. Praise ye the Lord! Oh, come to-day with sing-ing! Bless ye the Lord, all hon-or to Him bring-ing! Come, all ye chil-dren, His great love pro-claim, Kneel and a-dore Him, Ho-ly is His name!

2. Bow in His pres-ence, ask that He may guide you; Still, day and night, He ev-er walks be-side you. Come, all ye chil-dren, here His love pro-claim, Kneel and a-dore Him, Ho-ly is His name!

227

I Would Be True

Howard A. Walter, 1884-1918

Joseph Y. Peek, 1911

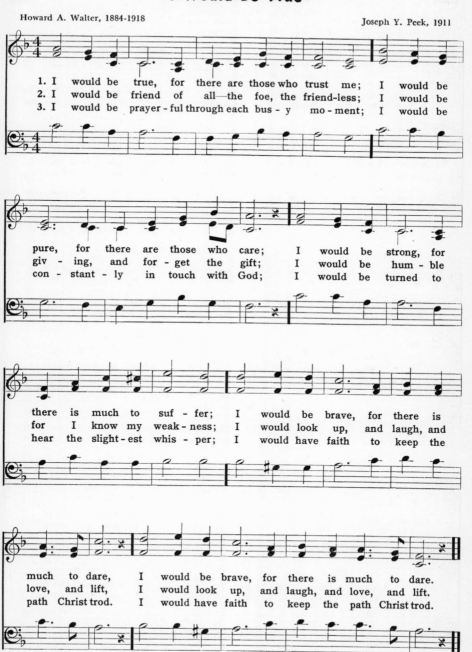

1. I would be true, for there are those who trust me; I would be
2. I would be friend of all—the foe, the friend-less; I would be
3. I would be prayer-ful through each bus-y mo-ment; I would be

pure, for there are those who care; I would be strong, for
giv-ing, and for-get the gift; I would be hum-ble
con-stant-ly in touch with God; I would be turned to

there is much to suf-fer; I would be brave, for there is
for I know my weak-ness; I would look up, and laugh, and
hear the slight-est whis-per; I would have faith to keep the

much to dare, I would be brave, for there is much to dare.
love, and lift, I would look up, and laugh, and love, and lift.
path Christ trod. I would have faith to keep the path Christ trod.

228 Lord, to Thy Name

NON NOBIS, DOMINE
(Canon for three voices)

Psalm 115: 1
Translation by K. D.

William Byrd, 1542-1623

last time

to Thy name be all the glo - ry.
no - bis Do - mi - ne, non no - bis.

Lord, to Thy name be all the glo - ry.
non no - bis, Do - mi - ne, non no - bis.

ev - er - more. Lord, to Thy name be all the glo - ry.
glo - ri - am, non no - bis, Do - mi - ne, non no - bis.

229   Thou Hast Built the Glorious Mountain

From the German   Gruenberger

Soprano 1 and 2

1. Thou hast built the glo-rious moun-tain, Shaped the riv - er's might - y bed,
2. Thou dost lead the flight of swal-lows, Thou dost show the stars their way;
3. All Thy crea-tures, Lord most ho - ly, Praise Thy name for - ev - er-more;

Alto

1. Thou hast built the glo-rious moun-tain, Shaped the riv - er's might - y bed,
2. Thou dost lead the flight of swal-lows, Thou dost show the stars their way;
3. All Thy crea-tures, Lord most ho - ly, Praise Thy name for - ev - er-more;

Optional Bass

Raised the hap - py leap - ing foun-tain, Made the flee - cy clouds o'er-head.
Sea - son af - ter sea - son fol-lows; Thou didst or - der night and day.
All Thy works, both high and low - ly, Tell Thy pow'r, Thy love a-dore.

Raised the hap - py leap-ing foun - tain, Made the flee - cy clouds o'er-head.
Sea - son af - ter sea-son fol - lows; Thou didst or - der night and day.
All Thy works, both high and low - ly, Tell Thy pow'r; Thy love a - dore.

230   All the People Praise Thee

St. Anthony's Chorale

With firmness and vigor

Joseph Haydn, 1732-1809

High voice
mf

Low voice

All Thy peo - ple praise Thee, praise Thee, Lord of our thanks-giv-ing,

Changed voice
mf

f

As we count our bless - ings, bless-ings, on this day of good-ness!

p

1. Gath - ered in the gold - en har - vest, Gar - nered in the sheaves of grain,
2. For Thy boun - ty, for Thy bless-ings Thank-ful songs to Thee we sing,

pp

Thanks to Thee, the boun-teous giv - er Toil has not been vain
Know - ing that the au - tumn har - vest Comes from Thee, our King.

f

All the peo - ple praise Thee, sing - ing, prais - es ev - er - more.

231

Lead, Kindly Light

John Henry Newman

John B. Dykes

1. Lead, kind - ly light! a - mid th' en-cir-cling gloom, Lead thou me on;
2. I was not ev - er thus, nor prayed that thou Shouldst lead me on;
3. So long thy pow'r has blest me, sure it still Will lead me on

The night is dark, and I am far from home, Lead thou me on;
I loved to choose and see my path, but now Lead thou me on;
O'er moor and fen, o'er crag and tor - rent till The night is gone,

Keep thou my feet; I do not ask to see
I loved the gar - ish day; and, spite of fears,
And with the morn those an - gel fac - es smile,

The dis - tant scene, one step e - nough for me.
Pride ruled my will; re - mem - ber not past years.
Which I have loved long since, and lost a - while.

232   As the Thirsty Hart Would Hasten

Psalm 42
Adapted from a French Metrical Version

French Chant

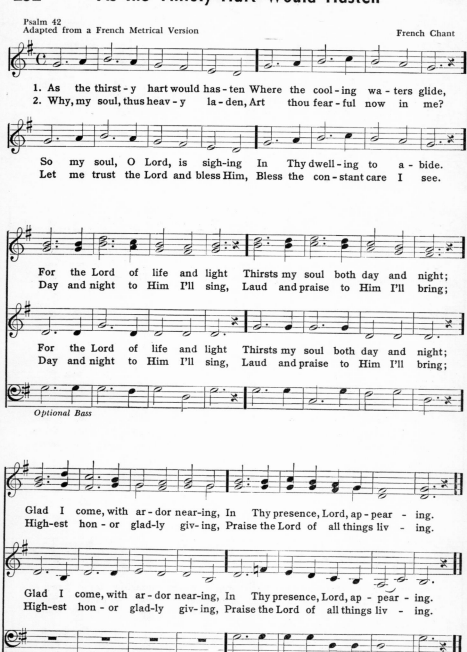

1. As the thirst-y hart would has-ten Where the cool-ing wa-ters glide,
2. Why, my soul, thus heav-y la-den, Art thou fear-ful now in me?

So my soul, O Lord, is sigh-ing In Thy dwell-ing to a - bide.
Let me trust the Lord and bless Him, Bless the con-stant care I see.

For the Lord of life and light Thirsts my soul both day and night;
Day and night to Him I'll sing, Laud and praise to Him I'll bring;

For the Lord of life and light Thirsts my soul both day and night;
Day and night to Him I'll sing, Laud and praise to Him I'll bring;

Optional Bass

Glad I come, with ar-dor near-ing, In Thy presence, Lord, ap-pear - ing.
High-est hon-or glad-ly giv-ing, Praise the Lord of all things liv - ing.

Glad I come, with ar-dor near-ing, In Thy presence, Lord, ap - pear - ing.
High-est hon-or glad-ly giv-ing, Praise the Lord of all things liv - ing.

233 # My Shepherd Leadeth Me

Psalm 23
Paraphrased by L. J. H.

Bortniansky, 1751-1825

1. My Shep-herd lead-eth me, I shall want not, For He makes me
2. Yea, though I walk in death's dark vale, I will not be a-

down to lie in green pas - tures; To qui - et wa - ters
fraid, For Thou art with me; Thy rod and staff they

He lead - eth me. My soul He re - stor - eth, re - stor - eth a-
com - fort me still, Yea though death's dark val - ley I walk I will

gain, And He mak - eth me to walk in paths of right - eous
not be a - fraid, For Thou art with me and Thy rod and Thy

I walk in paths of right - eous -
I will not fear, Thy rod and

ness, For His name's sake, For His name's sake. A - men, A - men.
staff they will com-fort, they will com - fort me.

ness
staff

234 O Power of Love

Gerhard Tersteegen, 1697-1769
Tr. H. Brueckner, alt.

Dimitri Bortniansky, 1751-1825
Arr. Howard Heise

Soprano and Alto

1. O pow'r of love, all else trans - cend - ing In Je - sus
2. Thou art my rest, no earth - ly treas - ure Can sat - is -
3. To Thee my heart and life be giv - en, Thou art in

Changed voices

pres - ent ev - er - more, I wor - ship Thee, in hom - age bend - ing,
fy my yearn-ing heart, And naught can give to me the pleas - ure
truth my high - est Good; For me Thy sa - cred side was riv - en

Thy name to hon - or and a - dore: Yea, let my soul, in
I find in Thee, my chos - en part, Thy love, so ten - der
For me was shed Thy pre - cious blood. O Thou who art the

deep de - vo - tion, Bathe in love's might - y bound-less o - cean.
so pos - sess - ing, Is joy to me, and ev - 'ry bless - ing.
world's sal - va - tion, Be Thine my love and ad - o - ra - tion.

235
God Is Our Refuge
(Integer Vitae)

Psalm 46

F. F. Flemming, 1810

Sopranos 1 and 2

1. God is our ref - uge, stead - fast and un - shak - en,
2. There - fore we fear not, sure of our sal - va - tion,
3. There is a riv - er, gent - ly on it glid - eth,

Alto

1. God is our ref - uge, stead - fast and un - shak - en,
2. There - fore we fear not, sure of our sal - va - tion,
3. There is a riv - er, gent - ly on it glid - eth,

Bass Optional

Shield-ing us safe - ly when the storms a - wak - en; Ne'er shall His
E'en though the moun - tains shake to their foun - da - tion; Though earth be
Wa - t'ring the cit - y where our Lord a - bid - eth; Who to its

Shield-ing us safe - ly when the storms a - wak - en; Ne'er shall His
E'en though the moun - tains shake to their foun - da - tion; Though earth be
Wa - t'ring the cit - y where our Lord a - bid - eth; Who to its

chil - dren be by Him for - sak - en; His hand sus - tains us.
mov - ed, fright-ened ev - 'ry na - tion, God's love is o'er us.
heal - ing all his ills con - fid - eth, Nev - er shall per - ish.

chil - dren be by Him for - sak - en; His hand sus - tains us.
mov - ed, fright-ened ev - 'ry na - tion, God's love is o'er us.
heal - ing all his ills con - fid - eth, Nev - er shall per - ish.

236
Send Out Thy Light

Arranged from an Anthem
by Charles Gounod

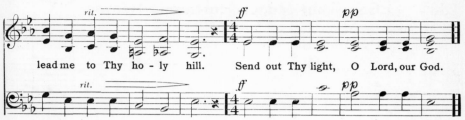

leadme to Thy ho - ly hill. Send out Thy light, O Lord, our God.

237 Peace Be With All

(Good-Night Song)

Stephen Fay, Alt.

Lithuanian Melody

Sopranos 1 and 2

1. Peace be with all, the peace from God our Fa - ther; Peace, heav'nly
2. Peace be with all, then e - vil can-not harm us; Peace, heav'nly

Alto

peace, at - tend us ev -'ry hour. Keep the heart of friend-ship beat - ing,
peace, that com-eth from a - bove. Tho' the ills of life as - sail us,

Peace— be

Peace—

And un - til an - oth - er meet - ing, Peace be with all.
God's pro - tec - tion will not fail us, Peace be with all.

with— all—

S.A.B.

238 God, That Madest Earth and Heaven

Reginald Heber, 1783-1836
William Mercer, 1864, *stanza 2*
Richard Whately, 1787-1863, *stanza 3*

Welsh Traditional Melody
Arr. Howard Heise, 1954

1. God, that mad-est earth and heav-en, Dark-ness and light;
2. And when morn a - gain shall call us To run life's way,
3. Guard us wak-ing, guard us sleep-ing, And when we die,

Who the day for toil hast giv-en, For rest the night;
May we still, what-e'er be-fall us, Thy will o - bey.
May we in Thy might-y keep-ing All peace-ful lie;

May Thine an - gel guards de-fend us, Slum-ber sweet Thy mer - cy send us;
From the power of e - vil hide us, In the nar-row path-way guide us,
When the last dread call shall wake us, Do not Thou, our God, for-sake us,

Ho - ly dreams and hopes at-tend us, This live - long night.
Nor Thy smile be e'er de-nied us, The live - long day.
But to reign in glo - ry take us, With Thee on high.

239   Holy God, We Praise Thy Name

Te Deum
Tr. Clarence Walworth   "Katholisches Gesangbuch", Vienna, 1774

1. Ho - ly God, we praise Thy name; Lord of all, we bow be - fore Thee.
2. Hark! the glad ce - les - tial hymn An - gel choirs a - bove are rais - ing;
3. Ho - ly, Fa - ther, Ho - ly Son, Ho - ly Spir - it, three we name Thee;

All on earth Thy scep - ter claim, All in heav'n a - bove a - dore Thee.
Cher - u - bim and ser - a - phim In un - ceas - ing cho - rus prais - ing
While in es - sence on - ly One, Un - di - vid - ed God we claim Thee.

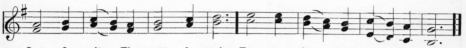

In - fi - nite Thy vast do - main, Ev - er - last - ing is Thy reign.
Fill the heav'ns with sweet ac - cord, Ho - ly, ho - ly, ho - ly Lord.
And a - dor - ing, bend the knee, While we sing our praise to Thee.

240   Rejoice, Ye Pure in Heart

Plumptre   Messiter
                                                 Arr. by I. W.

1. Re - joice, ye pure in heart! Re - joice, give thanks and sing!
2. Bright youth and snow-crowned age, Strong men and maid - ens meek
3. Yes, on through life's long path, Still chant - ing as ye go;
4. Then on, ye pure in heart, Re - joice, give thanks, and sing;

Your fes - tal ban - ner wave on high, The cross of Christ your King!
Raise high your free ex - ult - ing song! God's won - drous prais - es speak!
From youth to age, by night and day, In glad - ness and in woe.
Your glo - rious ban - ner wave on high, The Cross of Christ your King.

Re - joice! Re - joice!
Re - joice! Re - joice! Re - joice, give thanks and sing!

241   Give to Our God Immortal Praise

Isaac Watts

Arr. A. T. O.
in "Concord Series"

1. Give to our God im-mor-tal praise;
2. Give to the Lord of Lords re-nown;

Mer - cy and truth are all His
The King of kings with glo-ry

1. Give to our God im-mor-tal praise;
2. Give to the Lord of lords re-nown;

Mer -
The

ways; Hal-le - lu -jah, Hal-le - lu - jah! Won-ders of grace to God be -
crown: His mer-cies ev - er shall en -

cy and truth are all His ways; Hal-le - lu - jah!
King of kings with glo-ry crown; Won -
His

long, Re - peat your mer-cies in your song; Hal-le -
dure, When lords and kings are known no more:

ders of grace to God be - long, Re - peat His mer - cies in your
mer-cies ev - er shall en - dure, When lords and kings are known no

lu- jah, Hal - le - lu-jah! Hal-le - lu-jah, Hal-le - lu-jah, Hal-le - lu - jah!

song; Hal-le - lu-jah, Hal - le - lu - jah, Hal-le - lu-jah, Hal-le - lu - jah!
more:

3. He built the earth, He spread the sky,
And fixed the starry lights on high;
Wonders of grace to God belong
Repeat His mercies in your song;

242 Sing to the Lord

C. H. Hohman

Sing to the Lord a new-made song, and praise His name for - ev - er!

Sing to the Lord a new-made song, Sing to the Lord a new-made song.
Sing to the Lord a new-made song Sing to the Lord a

Sing to the Lord a new-made song Sing to the Lord, Sing to the
new-made song Sing to the Lord a song, Sing to the Lord,

Lord, Sing to the Lord, Sing to the Lord, all ye lands, to the
Sing to the Lord, Sing to the Lord, to the Lord, all ye lands,

Lord, all ye lands, to the Lord, all ye lands, and praise His name for-ev - er!
to the Lord, all ye lands, to the Lord Sing and praise His name for-ev - er!

243   Come, Pure Hearts

Latin 12th cent.
Tr. Robert Campbell, 1859, Alt.

Mozart

2part choir
String Trio optional

1. Come, pure hearts, in sweet - est meas-ure
2. See the riv - ers pour that glad - en,
3. O that we Thy truth con - fess - ing,

Sing of those who spread the treas-ure In the
With their streams the bet - ter E - den, Plant - ed
And Thy ho - ly word pos - sess-ing, Je - sus

ho - ly gos - pels shrined;
by our Lord most dear.
may Thy love a - dore:

Duet

Bless - ed ti - dings of sal -
Christ the foun - tain these the
Un - to Thee our voic - es

va - tion, Peace on earth their proc - la - ma - tion,
wa - ters; Drink O Si - on's sons and daugh-ters,
rais - ing, Thee with all Thy ran - somed prais-ing,

Love from God to lost man - kind,
Drink and find sal - va - tion here,
Ev - er and for - ev - er - more,

Repeat by Choir

Love from God to lost man - kind.
Drink and find sal - va - tion here.
Ev - er and for - ev - er - more.

244 O Lord, How Wondrous Thy Name

Psalm 8

Bach

O Lord, our Lord, how won-drous Thy name in all the earth:

The moon and stars Thou mad - est, Pro - claim Thy won - drous worth;

And man Thou crown'st with glo - ry and hon - or from his birth.

O Lord our Lord how won-drous, Thy name in all the earth.

245

Daughter of Zion

From *Judas Maccabaeus*
George Frederick Handel, 1685-1757

With 3 strings optional

1. Daugh - ter of Zi - on, Re - joice great - - ly,
2. Ho - si - an - na! Da - vid's roy - al Son,
3. Ho - si - an - na! Praise and prayer we bring,

Fine

Re - joice great - ly Daugh - ter of Je - ru - sa - lem.
Bless - ed are the peo - ple of the Ho - ly One.
Glo - ry, laud and hon - or To our gra - cious King.

Thy...... King now com - eth, com - eth un - to thee,
Let .... Thy King - dom ev - er - last - ing come,
Ev - - er - last - ing is Thy reign of love,

D. C.

Thy....... King now com - eth, com - eth un - to thee,
Ho - - si - an - na, King and bless - ed One.
Thou .... the Son of God en - throned a - bove.

246 The Daylight Fades

Thomas O. Sommers, 1849

1. The day-light fades, the eve-ning shades are gath-er-ing round my
2. While Thou art near I need not fear the gloom of mid - night
3. Par - don my sin, and en - ter in to sanc - ti - fy my

1. The day - light fades, eve - ning shades are gath - ering
2. While Thou art near I need not fear the gloom of
3. O par-don my sin, and en-ter in to sanc - ti -

head: Fa - ther a - bove, I praise Thy love which
hour: Blest Je - sus still from ev - 'ry ill de -
heart; Spir - it di - vine, O make me Thine, and

round, a - round my head: Fa - ther a - bove I praise Thy
mid - night, mid - night hour; Blest Je - sus, still from ev - 'ry
fy my heart, my heart: Spir - it Di - vine, O make me

night - ly guards my bed. Fa - ther a - bove,
fend me with Thy power! Blest Je - sus, still
Ne'er from me de - part! Spir - it Di - vine

love which guards my bed. O Fa - ther a - bove I praise Thy
ill de - fend, de - fend, O blest Je - sus, still from ev - 'ry
Thine, and never de - part, O Spir - it Di - vine O make me,

I praise Thy love which night - ly guards my bed
from ev - 'ry ill de - fend me with Thy power.
O make me Thine and ne'er from me de - part.

love, Thy love, I praise Thy love which guards my bed.
ill, from ill, Je - sus de - fend me with Thy power.
make me Thine, And ne'er from me, from me de - part.

247   Come, My Soul, Thou Must Be Waking

F. R. von Canitz, 1699

Franz Joseph Haydn

1. Come, my— soul, thou must be wak - ing, Now is break - ing O'er the
2. Pray that— He may pros - per ev - er Each en - deav - or, When thine
3. Think that— He thy ways be - hold - eth; He un - fold - eth Ev - 'ry
4. On - ly— God's free gifts a - buse not, Light re - fuse not, But His

earth an - oth - er day; Come to Him who made this splen-dor,
aim is good and true; But that He may ev - er thwart thee,
fault that lurks with - in; He the hid - den shame glossed o - ver
Spir - it's voice o - bey; Thou with Him shalt dwell, be - hold - ing

See thou ren - der All thy fee - ble strength can pay.
And con - vert thee, When thou e - vil would'st pur - sue.
Can dis - cov - er, And dis - cern each deed of sin.
Light en - fold - ing All things in un - cloud - ed day.

248   Lo! the Heavens Are Breaking

Anonymous

German Melody

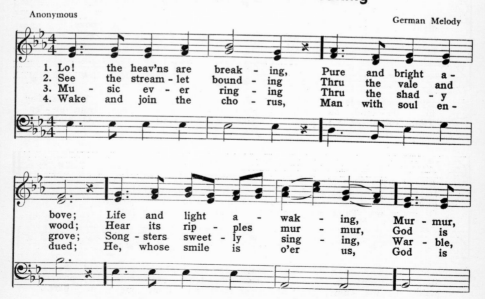

1. Lo! the heav'ns are break - ing, Pure and bright a -
2. See the stream - let bound - ing, Thru the vale and
3. Mu - sic ev - er ring - ing, Thru the shad - y
4. Wake and join the cho - rus, Man with soul en -

bove; Life and light a - wak - ing, Mur - mur,
wood; Hear its rip - ples mur - mur, God is
grove; Song - sters sweet - ly sing - ing, War - ble,
dued; He, whose smile is o'er us, God is

God is love, Mur - mur, God is love.
ev - er good, God is ev - er good.
God is love, War - ble, God is love.
ev - er good, God is ev - er good. A - men.

249 Away In a Manger

Traditional Carol

William James Kirkpatrick, 1838-1921

1. A - way in a man - ger, no crib for a bed, The lit - tle Lord
2. The cat - tle are low - ing, the ba - by a - wakes, But lit - tle Lord
3. Be near me, Lord Je - sus; I ask Thee to stay Close by me for -

Je - sus laid down His sweet head. The stars in the bright sky looked
Je - sus no cry - ing He makes. I love Thee, Lord Je - sus! look
ev - er, and love me I pray. Bless all the dear chil - dren in

down where He lay— The lit - tle Lord Je - sus a - sleep on the hay.
down from the sky, And stay by my cra - dle till morn - ing is nigh.
Thy ten - der care And fit us for heav - en to live with Thee there.

Another setting of this carol is found at No. 254.

250 Sing to the Lord

John S. B. Monsell, 1811-1875
Based on Psalm 145: 1-2

German Folk Song, c. 1800

1. Sing to the Lord a joy - ful song; Lift up your hearts, your
2. For life and love, for rest and food, For dai - ly help and

Sing to the Lord........

voi - ces raise; To us His gra - cious gifts be
night - ly care, Sing to the Lord for He is

long, To Him our songs, our songs of love and praise.
good, And praise His name, His name for it is fair.

To Him....

3. For strength to those who on Him wait,
   His truth to prove, His will to do,
   Praise ye our God, for He is great;
   Trust in His name, for it is true.

4. For joys untold, which from above
   Cheer those who love His high employ,
   Sing to our God, for He is love,
   Exalt His name, for it is joy.

251 Glory to God in the Highest

(Two-part Canon)

Old Canon

1. Glo - ry to God, to God in the high - est ev - er-more!
2. Peace up - on earth! yea, peace un - to all up - on the earth!
3. Good will to men! to all men good will, to all good will!

Glo - ry to God be ev - er more, be ev - er more!
Peace up - on earth yea, peace to all, to all man - kind!
To all is born the Sav - ior Je - sus Christ, the Lord.

(1) *and* (2) *after V. 3*

Hal - le - lu - jah! Hal - le - lu - jah! Hal - le - lu - jah!

252   The Lord Is My Shepherd

Psalm 23
James Montgomery, 1822   Thomas Koschat, 1862

Melody

1. The Lord is my Shep-herd, no want shall I know, I
2. Thru the val - ley and shad - ow of death though I stray, Since
3. In the midst of af - flic - tion my ta - ble is spread; With
4. Let good - ness and mer - cy, my boun - ti - ful God, Still

feed in green pas-tures, safe fold - ed I rest; He lead - eth my
Thou art my Guard-ian, no e - vil I fear; Thy rod shall de -
bless-ings un - meas-ured my cup run - neth o'er; With per-fume and
fol - low my steps till I meet Thee a - bove. I seek by the

soul where the still wa - ters flow, Re - stores me when wan-d'ring, re -
fend me, Thy staff be my stay; No harm can be - fall, with my
oil Thou a - noint - est my head; O what shall I ask of Thy
path which my fore - fa - thers trod, Thru the land of their so-journ, Thy

deems when op-pressed, Re - stores me when wan-d'ring, re-deems when op-pressed.
Com - fort - er near, No harm can be - fall, with my Com-fort-er near.
prov - i - dence more? O what shall I ask of Thy prov - i - dence more?
king - dom of love, Thru the land of their so-journ, Thy king-dom of love.

253 Now Are We the Sons of God

(Two-part Canon)

Martin Shaw

1st Soprano

Now are we the sons of God, now are we the sons of God, and it

2nd Soprano

Now are we the sons of God, now are we the sons of

doth not yet ap - pear what we shall be: But we

God, and it doth not yet ap - pear what we shall be.

know that we shall be like Him, that we shall be like

For we know that we shall be like Him, that

Him: For we shall see Him, we shall see Him as He is.

we shall be like Him: For we shall see Him, see Him as He is.

From "Songs of Praise for Children". Tune copyrighted by Oxford University Press. Used by permission.

254 Away in a Manger

Traditional Carol

Carl Mueller

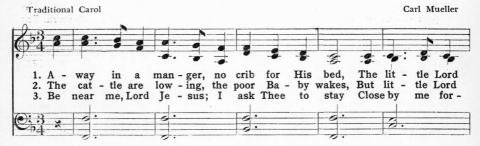

1. A - way in a man - ger, no crib for His bed, The lit - tle Lord
2. The cat - tle are low - ing, the poor Ba - by wakes, But lit - tle Lord
3. Be near me, Lord Je - sus; I ask Thee to stay Close by me for-

Je - sus laid down His sweet head. The stars in the sky looked
Je - sus, no cry - ing He makes. I love Thee, Lord Je - sus, look
ev - er, and love me I pray. Bless all the dear chil - dren in

down where He lay, The lit - tle Lord Je - sus, a - sleep on the hay.
down from the sky, And stay by my side un - til morn-ing is nigh.
Thy ten - der care And fit us for heav-en to live with Thee there. A - men.

255   O God, Beneath Thy Guiding Hand

Leonard Bacon   John Hatton

1. O God, be - neath Thy guid - ing hand, Our ex - iled
2. Thou heard'st well-pleased, the song, the prayer; Thy bless - ing
3. Laws, free - dom, truth, and faith in God Came with those
4. And here Thy name, O God of love, Their chil-dren's

fa - thers crossed the sea; And when they trod the
came, and still its pow'r Shall on - ward, through all
ex - iles o'er the waves, And, where their pil - grim
chil - dren shall a - dore, Till these e - ter - nal

win - try strand, With prayer and psalm they wor - shiped Thee.
a - ges bear The mem - 'ry of that ho - ly hour.
feet have trod, The God they trust - ed guards their graves.
hills re - move, And spring a - dorns the earth no more.

256 Great God, We Sing That Mighty Hand

Philip Doddridge, 1755

"Mendon," German melody
Arr. by Samuel Dyer, 1828
Arr. by H. Markworth

1. Great God, we sing that might - y hand By which sup -
2. By day, by night, at home, a - broad Still we are
3. With grate - ful hearts the past we own; The fu - ture,
4. When death shall in - ter - rupt our songs And seal in

1. Great God, we sing that hand
2. By day, night, home, a - broad,
3. With grate - ful hearts we own;
4. When death shall still our songs

1. port - ed still we stand. The op'n - ing year Thy
2. guard - ed by our God, By His in - ces - sant
3. all to us un - known, We to Thy guard - ian
4. si - lence mor - tal tongues, Our Help - er, God, in

1. By which sup - port we stand. The year Thy
2. Still guard - ed by our God, By con - stant
3. The fu - ture all un - known, We to Thy
4. And seal our mor - tal tongues, Our Help - er,

1. mer - cy shows; Let mer - cy crown it till it close.
2. boun - ty fed, By His un - err - ing coun - sel led.
3. care com - mit And, peace-ful, leave be - fore Thy feet.
4. whom we trust, In bet - ter worlds our soul shall boast.

1. mer - cy shows; And crown it till it close.
2. boun - ty fed, And by His coun - sel led.
3. care com - mit And leave be - fore Thy feet.
4. whom we trust, In worlds our soul shall boast.

NOTE: For variety it is suggested that some stanzas be sung in uinson by the sopranos.

257
Blow winds, O Softly Blow

Thomas Tiplady

German Folk Song

Refrain Blow, winds, O soft - ly blow; Bring flow-ers in - stead of snow;

Let blos-soms deck the trees A Babe to please.

Duet

1. The win - ter morn comes gent-ly down The qui - et streets of Da-vid's town,
2. Sing, an-gels, sing a lul - la - by Or He too soon may learn to cry:
3. Draw near, O shep - herds, to His bed, For lambs ye oft have nursed and fed;

And in a man-ger old and brown, A lit - tle Child is sleep - ing.
Yea sing the songs He knew on high, Lest He for heav'n be griev - ing.
And 'tis God's Lamb that lays His head With-in this hum - ble man - ger.

258

Jesus Arose

(Two-part Canon)

Soprano and Alto

Michael Praetorius, 1610

Je - sus a - rose   Je - sus a - rose
Je - sus a - rose   up from the

up from the grave   the Sav - ior   a - rose,   tri - umph-ant o'er
grave   the Sav - ior   a - rose   tri - umph-ant o'er foes

foes   Up from the grave   the Sav - ior   a - rose   Al -
up from the grave   the Sav - ior   a - rose   al - le - lu -

le - lu - ia,   Al - le - lu - ia   vic - to - rious o'er   death. He
ia,   Al - le - lu - ia!   Vic - to - rious o'er   death   He

reigns   a - bove   Al - le -   Al - le - lu - ia.
reigns   a - bove   Al - le -   Al - le - lu - ia.

From "Singt und Spielt" Vol. II. Velhagen & Klasing, Hannover.

Geh aus, mein Herz

259

Paul Gerhardt

August Harder, 1775-1813
Arr. Walter Rein

1. Geh aus, mein Herz, und su - che Freud in die - ser schö - nen Som - mer - zeit an dei - nes Got - tes—Ga - ben! Schau an der schö - nen Gär - ten Zier und sie - he, wie sie mir und dir sich aus - ge - schmücket ha - ben, sich aus - ge - schmücket ha - ben.

2. Die Bäume stehen voller Laub, das Erdreich decket seinen Staub mit einem grünen Kleide; Narzissus und die Tulipan, die ziehen sich viel schöner an als Salomonis Seide.

3. Die Lerche schwingt sich in die Luft, das Täublein fliegt aus seiner Kluft und macht sich in die Wälder; die hochbegabte Nachtigall ergötzt und füllt mit ihrem Schall Berg, Hügel, Tal und Felder.

4. Ich selber kann und mag nicht ruhn; des großen Gottes großes Tun erweckt mir alle Sinnen, ich singe mit, wenn alles singt, und lasse, was dem Höchsten klingt, aus meinem Herzen rinnen.

S. A.

260 See How Great a Flame Aspires

Charles Wesley, 1707-1788

Ascribed to
Samuel Webbe, 1740-1816

1. See how great a flame as - pires, Kin - dled by a
2. When He first the work be - gun, Small and fee - ble
3. Sons of God, your Sav - ior praise! He the door hath
4. Saw ye not the cloud a - rise, Lit - tle as a

spark of grace! Je - sus' love the na - tions fires,
was His day; Now the word doth swift - ly run,
o - pened wide; He hath giv'n the word of grace,
hu - man hand? Now it spreads a - long the skies,

Sets the king - doms on a blaze; To bring fire on
Now it wins its wid - 'ning way; More and more it
Je - sus' word is glo - ri - fied; Je - sus, might - y
Hangs o'er all the thirst - y land: Lo! the prom - ise

earth He came, Kin - dled in some hearts it is; O that
spreads and grows, Ev - er might - y to pre - vail, Sin's strong -
to re - deem, He a - lone the work hath wrought; Wor - thy
of a show'r Drops al - read - y from a - bove; But the

all might catch the flame, All par - take the glo - rious bliss!
holds it now o'er - throws, Shakes the trem - bling gates of hell.
is the work of Him, Him who spake a world from naught.
Lord will short - ly pour All the Spir - it of His love!

261   Holy, Holy, Holy

Samuel Wesley, 1766-1837

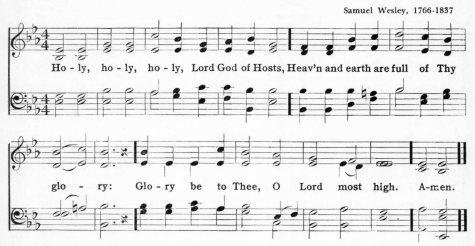

Ho - ly, ho - ly, ho - ly, Lord God of Hosts, Heav'n and earth are full of Thy glo - ry: Glo - ry be to Thee, O Lord most high. A-men.

262   The Lord Is in His Holy Temple

Call to Worship

George F. Root, 1820-1895

The Lord is in His ho - ly tem - ple, The Lord is in His ho - ly tem - ple, Let all the earth keep si - lence, Let all the earth keep si-lence be - fore Him, Keep si-lence, keep si-lence be - fore Him. A-men.

263

Holy, Holy, Holy

From The Holy City

Alfred R. Gaul

Ho - ly, Ho - ly, Ho - ly, Lord of Hosts;

Ho - ly, Ho - ly, Ho - ly is the Lord of Hosts.

264

Gloria Patri

Henry W. Greatorex, 1851

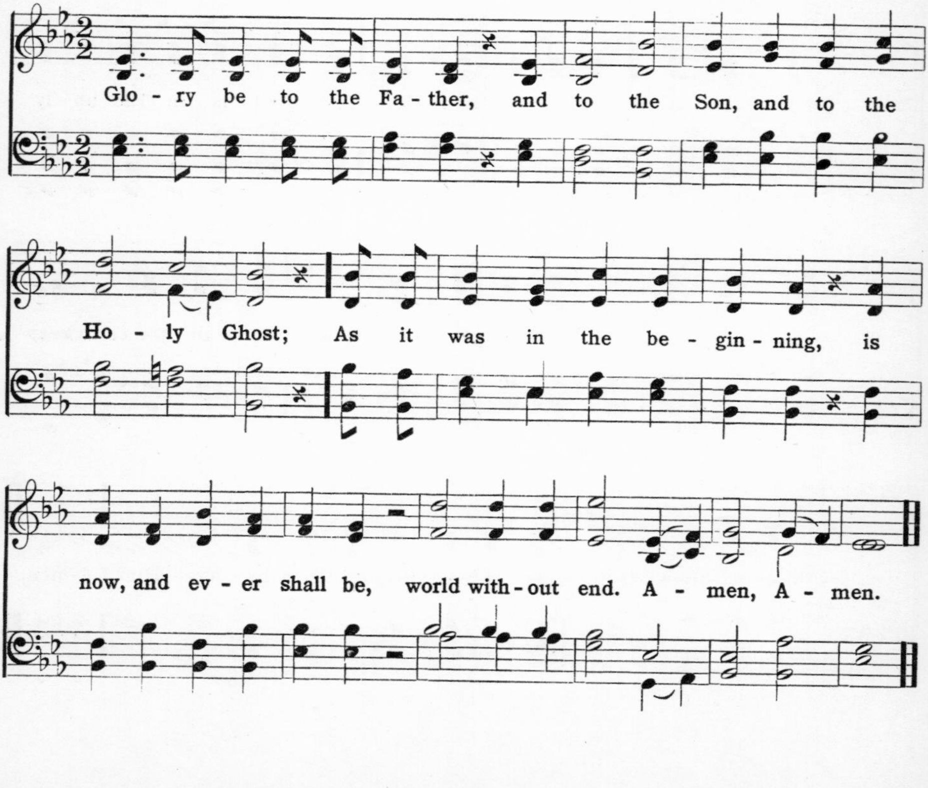

Glo - ry be to the Fa - ther, and to the Son, and to the

Ho - ly Ghost; As it was in the be - gin - ning, is

now, and ev - er shall be, world with - out end. A - men, A - men.

265

Hear Our Prayer, O Lord

George Whelpton

Hear our prayer, O Lord, Hear our prayer, O Lord;

In - cline Thine ear to us, And grant us Thy peace. A-men.

266*

Bless the Lord, O My Soul

Minister: Behold the tabernacle of God is with men, and He shall dwell with them, and they shall be His people, and God Himself shall be with them and be their God.

Choir:

Ippolitoff-Ivanoff

p Very slowly

Bless the Lord, O . . . . . my soul, Bless-ed art Thou, O Lord.

Minister: The Lord is nigh unto all that call upon Him, to all that call upon Him in truth. He will hear their cry and will save them.

Choir:

mf

p

Bless the Lord, O . . . . . . my soul and all that

pp rit.

is with - in me bless His ho - ly Name Bless the Lord, O my soul.

*These Responses may be used separately or together.

267   Spirit of the Living God

Daniel Iverson, 1926   Daniel Iverson, 1926

Spir-it of the liv-ing God, Now de-scend on me! Spir-it of the

liv-ing God, Now de-scend on me! Break me, melt me, Mould me,

fill me! Spir-it of the liv-ing God, Now de-scend on me! A-men.

268   Peace of the River

Glendore Gosling   Viola Wood
P, slowly, with expression

Peace, I ask of thee, O Riv - er, Peace, peace, peace.
When I learn to live se - rene - ly Cares will cease.

From the hills I gath - er cour - age, Vi - sion of the day to be,
Strength to lead and faith to fol - low, All are giv - en un - to me.

Peace I ask of thee, O Riv - er Peace, peace, peace.

269   # Let the Words of My Mouth

Edward Boatner, Alt.

Let the words of my mouth, med-i-
Let the words of my mouth, and the med-i-

ta-tion of my heart   Be ac-cep-ta-ble in Thy
ta-tion of my heart   Be ac-cep-ta-ble in Thy

sight, O Lord, my strength, And my Re-deem-er. A - men.

270   # Father, Bless the Gifts We Bring Thee

Presentation of Offering

Fliedner's Song Book, 1842

Fa-ther, bless the gifts we bring Thee; Give them some-thing kind to do;

May they help some-one to love Thee: Fa-ther, may we love Thee too. A-men.

271 Lord, Thou Dost Love the Cheerful Giver

Presentation of Offering (v. 1)

Robert Murray, 1880

Plymouth Collection

f All voices in unison

1. Lord, Thou dost love the cheer-ful giv - er, Who with o - pen heart and hand
2. Thine own life Thou free - ly gav - est As an of - fering on the cross
3. Sav - iour, Thou hast free - ly giv - en All the bless-ings we en - joy,

mf Women's voices

Bless - es free - ly, as a riv - er That re - fresh - es all the land;
For all sin - ners whom Thou sav-est From e - ter - nal shame and loss.
Earth - ly store and bread of heav-en, Love and peace with-out al - loy;

mf In harmony

Grant us, then, the grace of giv - ing With a spir - it large and free,
Blest by Thee with gifts and grac - es, May we heed Thy Church-'s call,
Hum - bly now we bow be - fore Thee, And our all to Thee re - sign;

p In harmony

That our life and all our liv - ing We may con - se - crate to Thee.
Glad-ly in all times and plac - es Give to Thee, who giv-est all.
For the king - dom, power, and glo - ry Are, O Lord, for - ev - er Thine. A-men.

272

Back of the Loaf

Maltbie D. Babcock

Anonymous

Back of the loaf is the snow-y flour, Back of the flour the mill;

Back of the mill the wheat, the show'r, The sun, and our Fa-ther's will.

Words reprinted from *Thoughts for Everyday Living* by Maltbie D. Babcock. Copyright 1901 by Charles Scribner's Sons, 1929 by Katherine T. Babcock. Used by permission of the publishers.

273

Lead Me, Lord

Psalm 4: 8; 5: 8

Samuel S. Wesley, 1810-1876

Slowly

Lead me, Lord, lead me in Thy right-eous-ness; Make Thy way

plain be-fore my face. For it is Thou, Lord, Thou Lord

on-ly that mak-est me dwell in safe-ty. A-men.

274

Sweep Over My Soul

Arr. Harold Moyer

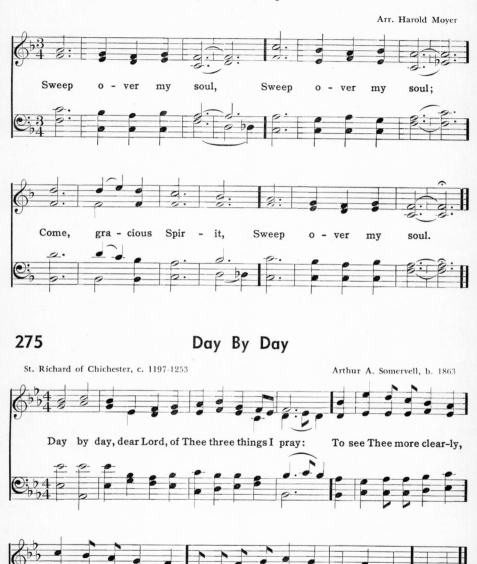

Sweep o - ver my soul, Sweep o - ver my soul;

Come, gra - cious Spir - it, Sweep o - ver my soul.

275

Day By Day

St. Richard of Chichester, c. 1197-1253

Arthur A. Somervell, b. 1863

Day by day, dear Lord, of Thee three things I pray: To see Thee more clear-ly,

Love Thee more dear - ly, Fol-low Thee more near-ly, Day by day. A-men.

276   Glory to God in the Highest

Canon for four voices.   Ludwig Ernst Gebhardi, 1787-1862

Glo - ry to God in the high - est! Peace on the

earth and good - will tow'rd men, Peace on earth and good

will and good will. A - - men. A - - men.

277   O Worship the Lord

Worship

Double Canon

O wor - ship the Lord, For He is our God; And

we are His peo - ple, The folk of His pas - ture, O

wor - ship the Lord, Our Mak - er our God, our God.

278   Tallis' Canon

Thomas Ken, 1695   Thomas Tallis, 1565

Glo - ry to Thee, my God, this night, For all the bless-ings of the light;

Keep me, oh keep me, King of Kings, Be-neath Thine own Al-might - y wings.

279 The Lord Is My Shepherd

Four-part canon

The Lord is my Shep-herd, my Guard-ian, my Guide, What-so-
ev - er I want, He doth kind - ly pro - vide, Ev - er
since I was born, it is He that hath crowned the life that He
gave me with bless-ings all round— The life that He gave me with
bless-ings, with bless-ings, With bless-ings, with bless-ings all round.

280 All Creatures of Our God and King

Two-part canon
St. Francis of Assissi

Lasst uns erfreuen

Old German Melody

1. All crea-tures of our God and King, Lift up your voice and with us
2. sing, Al - le - lu - ia, Al - le - lu - ia. The burn - ing sun with
gold - en beam, The sil - ver moon with soft - er gleam, O praise Him,
O praise Him, Al - le - lu - ia, Al - le - lu - ia, Al - le - lu - ia.

281

Dona Nobis Pacem!
(Give us Peace!)

Three-part canon

Composer unknown

Do - na no - bis pa - cem, pa - cem, do - na no - bis pa - cem.

Do - na no - bis pa - cem, do - na no - bis pa - - cem.

Do - na no - bis pa - cem, do - na no - bis pa - - cem.

282

Lobe den Herren!
(Praise to the Lord!)

Four-part canon

Composer unknown

Lo - be den Her - ren, den mäch - ti - gen Kö - nig der
Praise to the High - est, the Lord God give thanks, praise and

Eh - re! Stimm froh - lok - kend mit ein in die himm - li - schen
glo - ry! Let us sing joy - ful songs with the heav - en - ly

Chö - re! See - le, dein Dank schal - le mit fro - hem Ge -
choirs! Sing to the Lord, sing to the Lord and give

sang dei - nem Er - hal - ter zur Eh - re, zur Eh - re!
thanks. O praise the High-est, sing prais - es, Sing prais - es!

283

Rise Up, O Flame

Eight-part Round

Christoph Praetorius

Rise up, O flame, By thy light glow - ing,

Show to us beau - ty, Vi - sion and joy.

284 For Health and Strength

For health and strength and dai - ly food we give Thee thanks, O Lord. For

(NOTE: Sing as a round, twice through.)

285 O Give Thanks
(Round)

O give thanks, O give thanks, O give thanks un - to the Lord, for He is

gra-cious and His mer - cy en - dur - eth, en - dur - eth for - ev - er.

286 Morning, Evening
(Round)

Morn - ing, eve - ning, noon and night, For all Thy gifts We thank Thee, Lord.

287 Praise for Bread
(Round)

Morn - ing)
Noon - tide has come, the ta - ble spread. Thanks be to
Eve - ning)

Him who giv - eth bread, Praise God for bread.

288 Praise We the Father
(Round)

Praise we the Fa - ther, by whom we are fed; Thank Him for

giv - ing us dai - ly our bread. Praise Him, Praise Him, Praise Him for bread.

289

Come to Him

Three-part canon
Matt. 11: 28

Friedrich Kuhlau, 1786-1832

Come to Him! all who la-bor and are heav-y la-den, He will

give you rest. For He is meek and low-ly, For He is

meek and low-ly Come un-to Him all ye that

la-bor and come all ye heav-y la-den and He will

give you rest.............. and He will give you rest.

He is meek and low-ly of..... heart, and He will give you

rest, For His yoke is eas-y and His bur-den is light.

290

A Stranger At the Door

Three-part canon

Friedrich Kuhlau, 1786-1832

Be-hold a stran-ger at the door! He gen-tly knocks, has knock'd be-fore.

O love-ly, love-ly Stran-ger! Come in-to my heart to-day.

O love-ly Stran-ger come in, Come in-to my heart, Come in to stay.

291 Easter Bells

Three-part canon

Jakob Gottfried Farrari, 1759-1842

Ring out sweet bells of Eas-ter, To greet this joy-ful day;
While in the gold-en sun-shine, The hap-py chil-dren say:

The Lord now is ris-en, Glad mes-sage we will sing,
The Lord now is ris-en, Let Eas-ter bells now ring.

Ding dong, ding dong, sweet bells, now ring.

292 Alleluia

Three-part canon

Mozart

Al-le-lu-ia, Al-le-lu-ia. Praise to the Fa-ther,

O most Ho-ly, Be Thou ex-alt-ed, Lord most high. Sing al-le-

lu-ia, To the Fa-ther, Sing al-le-lu-ia to the Lord.

293 Hear the Echo

Three-part canon

Cherubini

Ha! ha! Ha! Ha! ha! ha! Ha! ha! ha! Hear the

ech-o, hear the ech-o as we sing. Let us joy-ful

joy-ful be, For we are chil-dren of the King.

294   Thanks Be to God

Four-part canon

Johann Fr. Reichardt, 1752-1814

Thanks be to God, our gracious Redeemer, O sing now His praises For He is kind and His mer-cy nev-er fail-eth, His truth en-dur-eth for ev-er.

295   Light from Above

Canon for three groups of four parts each

Mozart

Soprano: O, Ho-ly Spir-it, Light from a-bove...... Shine! shine!

Alto: O, Ho-ly Spir-it, Light from a-bove...... Shine! shine!

Tenor: O, Ho-ly Spir-it, Light from a-bove...... Shine! shine!

Bass: O Ho-ly Spir-it, Light from a-bove Shine! Send

Send us Thy Light! Shine! Light from a-bove Shine! shine!

Send us Thy Light! shine! Light from a-bove, shine!

Send........ us....... Thy Light! Shine! Shine!

us Thy Light! Shine! Light from a-bove, shine! Shine!

*Close with the three groups singing the first four bars.

296 Awake, My Soul

Canon for two parts
Thomas Ken

Johann Jakob Wachsmann, 1791-1853

1. A - wake, my soul, and with the sun Thy dai - ly stage of du - ty run.
2. Shake off dull sloth, and joy - ful rise To pay thy morn-ing sac - ri- fice.

297 Birthday

Four-part canon

Moritz Hauptman, 1792-1868

We wish you joy on this your birth - day,

And may God be with you ev - 'ry day.

298 Lord, Who Shall Live With Thee

Psalm 15: 1
Canon for three parts

Ludwig von Beethoven, 1770-1826

Lord, who shall live with Thee a guest? Who with Thee shall dwell?

E'en he who walks an up - right life, Who doth good

deeds and truth doth tell, and he the truth doth tell. The

man who lives with Thee as guest, He will be sure - ly blest.

299 Give to Our God Immortal Praise

Four-part canon

Ludwig Ernst Gebhardi, 1787-1862

Give to God im - mor - tal praise, glo - ry and hon - or;

Praise our God for - ev - er. A - men, A - men. A - men, A - men.

300 We Thank Thee Loving Father

Anon.   Traditional German Melody

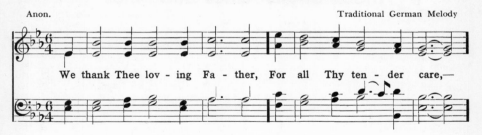

We thank Thee lov - ing Fa - ther, For all Thy ten - der care,—

For food and clothes and shel - ter And all the world so fair. A - men.

301 Day Is Done, Gone the Sun

Anonymous   TAPS. Irregular

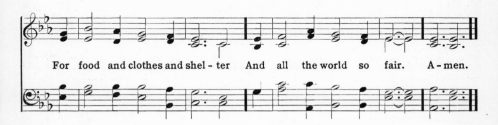

Day is done, gone the sun, from the lake, from the hills, from the

sky, Safe - ly rest, all is well, God is nigh.

302 Dresden Amen   303 Threefold Amen

A - men, A - men.

A - men, A - men, A - men.

Index of First Lines and Titles

(Titles in Capital Letters)